ELECTRONIC PROPERTIES OF AROMATIC AND HETEROCYCLIC MOLECULES

A Series of Monographs

THEORETICAL CHEMISTRY

Consulting Editor

D. P. CRAIG

Department of Chemistry, University College London England

Volume 1

T. E. PEACOCK: Electronic Properties of Aromatic and Heterocyclic Molecules

Forthcoming Volumes

E. STEWART: The Spectra of Small Polyatomic Molecules

A. C. HURLEY: The Electronic Theory of Small Molecules

R. MCWEENY and B. T. SUTCLIFFE: Introduction to the Methods of Quantum Chemistry

---

ELECTRONIC PROPERTIES OF AROMATIC AND HETEROCYCLIC MOLECULES

T. E. PEACOCK
King's College, University of London
England

1965

ACADEMIC PRESS
London and New York

ACADEMIC PRESS INC. (LONDON) LTD
Berkeley Square House
Berkeley Square
London, W.1

U.S. Edition published by
ACADEMIC PRESS INC.
111 Fifth Avenue
New York, New York 10003

Library of Congress Catalog Card Number: 65–26775

Printed in Great Britain by
Spottiswoode, Ballantyne and Company Limited
London and Colchester

Preface

The purpose of this book is to discuss the methods available for calculating the electron distribution and the electronic ground states of aromatic and heterocyclic molecules. There is also some discussion of the π-electronic spectra of these molecules. The accent of the book is on methods. There is, therefore, no attempt to give a detailed bibliography of the work that has appeared in this field over the last thirty years. Such bibliographies may be found in the books by A. Streitweiser, Jr., and by Jaffe and Orchin, referred to in the text.

It is assumed that the reader already has some acquaintance with the theory of valence. A knowledge at the level of C. A. Coulson's "Valence" (Oxford University Press) is adequate for an understanding of this book. It is also desirable, but not essential, that the reader should be to some extent conversant with the theory of matrices.

Chapter 1, on the many-electron atom, is not essential to the rest of the work. It is convenient to give a short description of this field, since the molecular self-consistent field theory is parallel to the theory in the atomic case. The reader may prefer to omit this chapter and commence reading at Chapter 2. He will, however, find that he is occasionally referred back to equations in Chapter 1.

The rest of the book is essentially a description of methods. The reader is led from the early theory of Hückel over the developments of the next thirty-four years to the most sophisticated theories now used to discuss the properties of this important class of molecule. While the main concern of the book is with molecular orbital theory, a whole chapter is nevertheless devoted to valence bond theory. The various models and their applications to the calculations of electronic properties are illustrated with respect to two series of molecules. The series chosen are the polyacene series and the nitrogen heterocyclic derivatives of benzene. These series are chosen because they represent typical molecules of each type. Consideration of these series also allows us to exploit the variation of some property with increasing number of rings or, on the other hand, with increasing number of nitrogen atoms in the benzene ring. It also allows direct comparison between values obtained using different methods.

There is no discussion in this volume of aromatic ions and radicals. The inclusion of such a discussion was contemplated originally, but it became apparent at an early date that this would almost double the size of the book. Perhaps at a later date another volume may be written that covers this field.

I should like to thank Professor D. P. Craig of University College London, who has shown continual interest in this volume and who has read parts of the manuscript and made valuable suggestions for its improvement. I also wish to thank my own research students at King's College, London, with whom I have discussed many of the problems that have arisen in this field. In particular, I should like to thank my first research student, Dr. P. T. Wilkinson, whose work on the polyacenes plays a large part in the discussion in the second part of this book, and whose conversations with me have been of the greatest assistance. My thanks are due also to my colleagues on the staff of King's College, London, many of whose comments are reflected in the ideas found within these pages.

T. E. Peacock

King's College
University of London
June 1965

Contents

Chapter 4

Improved Hückel Models

Chapter 5

The Self-consistent Field Theory

Chapter 6

Molecular Ground States

Chapter 7

Electronic Spectra—I

Chapter 8

Electronic Spectra—II

CHAPTER 1

The Many-electron Atom

Before discussing the electronic structure of the many-electron molecule it is necessary to discuss the structure of the many-electron atom. There are two reasons for this. Firstly, the molecular orbital theory is a direct extension of the theory of atomic orbitals. Secondly, much of the theory of many-electron atoms carries over into molecular orbital theory, and it seems worth while to deal with those concepts in the framework of the atomic theory.

1. The One-electron Atom

The one-electron atom is one of the few problems that can be solved in closed analytical form. We shall have occasion in much of what follows to use one-electron orbitals as a basis for molecular orbital calculations.

Consider an atom having one electron and nuclear charge Z; the Hamiltonian for the system is (in atomic units)

$$h = -\tfrac{1}{2}\nabla^2 - Z/r \qquad (1)$$

where $-\frac{1}{2}\nabla^2$ is the kinetic energy operator for the electron i, and r is the distance between the electron and the nucleus. Solution of the wave equations (2) gives us a set of eigenvalues, stationary states or orbital energies. These equations are

$$h\psi_i = E_i\psi_i \qquad (i=1,2,3\ldots) \qquad (2)$$

The eigenfunctions ψ_i are known as atomic orbitals, and in particular as hydrogen-like atomic orbitals, as they are the functions which describe the behaviour of a single electron moving in the field of a single atomic nucleus, and are therefore similar to the orbitals for the hydrogen atom.

2. The Many-electron Atom

The Hamiltonian for an N-electron system is given by

$$h = \sum_{i=1}^{N} (-\tfrac{1}{2}\nabla_i^2 - Z/r_i) + \tfrac{1}{2}\sum_{i,j=1}^{N} 1/r_{ij} \qquad (3)$$

If as a first approximation the second term is ignored, the eigenvalue problem becomes

$$\sum_{i=1}^{N} (-\tfrac{1}{2}\nabla^2 - Z/r_i)\psi = E\psi \tag{4}$$

which is separable into N equations each of type (2). The electrons are then allocated to one-electron orbitals, and a typical solution of (4) will be

$$\Psi = \psi_1(1)\psi_2(2)\psi_3(3)\ldots\psi_N(N) \tag{5}$$

Equation (5) is, however, still unsatisfactory because

(i) it ignores spin,
(ii) it does not treat indistinguishable electrons symmetrically.

Adding spin factors η_i, η_j $(= \alpha, \beta)$ will give an equation

$$\Psi = \psi_1(1)\eta(1)\psi_2(2)\eta(2)\ldots\psi_N(N)\eta(N) \tag{5a}$$

This is still unsatisfactory because it ignores indistinguishability. This can be taken into account by writing a wave function which allows the electrons to be permuted among all of the available orbitals. Such an equation would be

$$\Psi = \frac{1}{\sqrt{N}} \sum_i P_i \psi_1(1)\eta(1)\psi_2(2)\eta(2)\ldots\psi_N(N)\eta(N) \tag{5b}$$

This equation is still unsatisfactory although it takes both electron pin and indistinguishability into consideration. It is an empirical fact that electrons, like all particles which have half integral spin eigenvalues, are antisymmetric with respect to particle interchange. A satisfactory wave function will be of the form

$$\Psi = \frac{1}{\sqrt{N}} \sum_i P_i(-1)^i \psi_1(1)\eta(1)\psi_2(2)\eta(2)\ldots\psi_N(N)\eta(N) \tag{5c}$$

The most convenient way of representing an antisymmetric function is as a determinant (Slater, 1929). Function (5c) then becomes

$$\Psi_0 = \frac{1}{\sqrt{N}} \begin{vmatrix} \psi_1(1)\alpha(1) & \psi_1(1)\beta(1) & \ldots & \psi_{N/2}(1)\beta(1) \\ \psi_1(2)\alpha(2) & \psi_1(2)\beta(2) & \ldots & \psi_{N/2}(2)\beta(2) \\ \vdots & & & \\ \psi_1(N)\alpha(N) & \psi_1(N)\beta(N) & \ldots & \psi_{N/2}(N)\beta(N) \end{vmatrix} \tag{6}$$

Such a function would then be a satisfactory description of the ground state of the atom.

It is convenient to define a set of spin orbitals which are defined by

$$\phi_i = \psi_i \alpha$$

and

$$\bar{\phi}_i = \psi_i \beta$$

Then (6) becomes

$$\Psi_0 = \frac{1}{\sqrt{N}} \begin{vmatrix} \phi_1(1) & \bar{\phi}_1(1) & \dots & \bar{\phi}_{N/2}(1) \\ \phi_1(2) & \bar{\phi}_1(2) & \dots & \bar{\phi}_{N/2}(2) \\ \vdots & & & \\ \phi_1(N) & \bar{\phi}_1(N) & \dots & \bar{\phi}_{N/2}(N) \end{vmatrix} \tag{6a}$$

Ψ vanishes unless all columns are independent and this means that, in the ground state, the orbitals with lowest energy are filled with only two electrons each, or one in each spin orbital. Such a formulation is merely an expression of the well-known Pauli exclusion principle.

We now consider the case where our N electrons are allocated two at a time to the $N/2$ lowest-lying orbitals, i.e. the ground state. In an analytical approach to the many-electron atom problem we use a product of one-electron atomic orbitals (which may be a set of hydrogen-like functions in which the effective nuclear charge Z may be regarded as a variational parameter) carefully chosen so as to obtain the best approximation to the problem in which electron interaction is included. The best atomic orbitals are then determined by solution of a one-electron problem with a certain "effective" Hamiltonian.

The energy of the system (assuming the one-electron functions to be orthonormal) is given by

$$E = \int \Psi_0^* h \Psi_0 \, d\tau \tag{7}$$

Substitution from (3) and (6) gives

$$E = 2 \sum_i f_i + \sum_{i,j} (2J_{ij} - K_{ij}) \tag{8}$$

where

$$f_i = \int \psi_i^*(1) \left| -\tfrac{1}{2}\nabla_i^2 - \frac{Z}{r_i} \right| \psi_i \, d\tau_i \tag{8}$$

is the one-electron contribution to the energy from electron i, and the two-electron contribution is given in terms of the "Coulomb" and exchange integrals J and K which are defined by

$$J_{ij} = \int \psi_i^*(1)\, \psi_j^*(2) \left| \frac{1}{r_{12}} \right| \psi_i(1)\, \psi_j(2) \, dv_1 \, dv_2 \tag{9}$$

$$K_{ij} = \int \psi_i^*(1)\, \psi_j^*(2) \left| \frac{1}{r_{12}} \right| \psi_j(1)\, \psi_i(2) \, dv_1 \, dv_2 \tag{10}$$

and by definition $J_{ii} = K_{ii}$.

This expression can be written in terms of Coulomb and exchange operators,

$$J = \sum_i J_i \quad \text{and} \quad K = \sum_i K_i$$

where $$J_i\psi_i(1) = \left(\int \psi_i^*(2)|g|\psi_i(2)\,dv_2\right)\psi_j(1) \quad \left(\text{where } g = \frac{1}{r_{12}}\right) \tag{11}$$

and

$$K_i\psi_j(1) = \left(\int \psi_i^*(2)|g|\psi_j(2)\,dv_2\right)\psi_i(1) \tag{12}$$

The Hartree–Fock Hamiltonian operator may then be written

$$\mathbf{h}^F = \mathbf{f} + 2\mathbf{J} - \mathbf{K} = \mathbf{f} + \mathbf{G} \tag{13}$$

The total energy is then given by (Slater, 1929)

$$E = \sum_i \int \psi_i^*(2f + 2J - K)\psi_i\,dv = \sum_i \psi_i^*(2h^F - G)\psi_i\,dv \tag{14}$$

and by the variation method it is easily shown that the best orbitals are solutions of the one-electron eigenvalue equation (15), and because the operator is Hermitian they are orthogonal and are usually normalized to unity.

$$\mathbf{h}^F\mathbf{\Psi} = \mathbf{E}\mathbf{\Psi} \tag{15}$$

This many-electron Hamiltonian may be used to calculate an atomic self-consistent field in which the charge distribution and the associated potential field are self-consistent.

3. The Self-consistent Field Process

The energy expression is

$$E = 2\sum_i \psi_i^* f\psi_i + \sum_i \psi_i^* G\psi_i \tag{16}$$

where i runs over all occupied orbitals.

The usual variation process of letting $\psi_i \to \psi_i + \delta\psi_i$ is allowed subject to the retention of orthonormality as an auxiliary condition. This leads to

$$\sum_i \delta\psi_i^*[(f\psi_i + G\psi_i) - \sum_j \psi_j(\epsilon)_{ji}] = 0 \tag{17}$$

and a similar conjugate equation. $(\epsilon)_{ji}$ is a matrix of Lagrangian multipliers. Since the variations are, in effect, arbitrary, the vanishing of the scalar products implies the vanishing of each vector

$$f\psi_i + G\psi_i - \sum_j \psi_j(\epsilon)_{ji} = 0 \quad (\text{arbitrary } \psi_i) \tag{18}$$

Now

$$\epsilon_{ij} = \int \psi_i^* h^F \psi_j\,dv = \int \psi_i^* f\psi_j\,dv + 2\int \psi_i J\psi_j\,dv - \int \psi_i K\psi_j\,dv \tag{19}$$

By a suitable linear transformation we can put $(\epsilon)_{ji}$ into diagonal form. The system of linear equations then reduces to

$$\left.\begin{aligned} h^F \psi_i' &= (\epsilon)_{ii}\psi_i' \\ h^F \psi_j' &= (\epsilon)_{jj}\psi_j' \end{aligned}\right\} \tag{20}$$

The new ψ' which are formed out of the ψ are an improved set of eigenfunctions. Repetition of the process leads to self-consistency between the eigenfunctions and the Hamiltonian.

In practice the procedure is as follows. We calculate the elements of the Hamiltonian from our trial wave functions. We then find the eigenvalues of the set of simultaneous equations

$$\sum_j (h_{ij} - S_{ij} E) c_j = 0 \quad (i = 1, 2 \ldots n) \tag{21}$$

where

$$h_{ij} = \int \psi_i h^F \psi_j \, dv \quad \text{and} \quad S_{ij} = \int \psi_i^* \psi_j \, dv$$

The condition that leads to a non-trivial solution of the set of equations is that

$$|h_{ij} - S_{ij}\epsilon| = 0 \tag{22}$$

From this we can determine the spectrum of eigenvalues, and by substituting into the set of equations we can find the revised set of eigenfunctions. These may be used to calculate a new Hamiltonian using (13) and the process repeated until self-consistency is achieved. The above set of equations is known as the secular equation and the associated determinant as the secular determinant. Other methods are available to solve the eigenvalue problem and these will be discussed in a later chapter.

An immediate problem is to see if there are any ways in which we can reduce the size of the secular determinant, since this is frequently laborious to evaluate.

4. Angular Momentum and the Reduction of the Secular Problem

Our eigenfunctions are characterized by four quantum numbers, n, m, m_z and s_z. m and m_z are the orbital angular momentum and its projection on the z-axis respectively. s_z is the component of the spin angular momentum along the z-axis. They are the eigenvalues of the corresponding operators. M is the orbital angular momentum operator and M_x, M_y and M_z are its components. From the vector nature of angular momentum we can write

$$m = (m_x^2 + m_y^2 + m_z^2)^{\frac{1}{2}}$$

In an N-electron system, each electron will be characterized by a set of angular momentum quantum numbers. The corresponding quantities M, M_x, M_y and M_z are then defined by

$$\left.\begin{aligned} M_x &= \sum_i m_{xi} \\ M_y &= \sum_i m_{yi} \\ M_z &= \sum_i m_{zi} \\ \text{and} \qquad M^2 &= M_x^2+M_y^2+M_z^2 \end{aligned}\right\} \tag{23}$$

where the summation runs over all of the electrons in the system.

A similar set of equations relates the eigenvalues of the spin operators for the individual electrons to the total spin eigenvalues.

$$\left.\begin{aligned} S_x &= \sum_i s_{ix} \\ S_y &= \sum_i s_{iy} \\ S_z &= \sum_i s_{iz} \\ S^2 &= S_x^2+S_y^2+S_z^2 \end{aligned}\right\} \tag{24}$$

The total angular momentum for an electron i is given by

$$j = m+s$$

The total angular momentum for the N-electron atom and its components is then given by

$$\left.\begin{aligned} J_x &= M_x+S_x \\ J_y &= M_y+S_y \\ J_z &= M_z+S_z \\ J^2 &= J_x^2+J_y^2+J_z^2 \end{aligned}\right\} \tag{25}$$

We also have certain relations between the components of M,

$$\left.\begin{aligned} M_x M_y - M_y M_x &= ihM_z \\ M_y M_z - M_z M_y &= ihM_x \\ M_z M_x - M_x M_z &= ihM_y \end{aligned}\right\} \tag{26}$$

Similar relations hold between the components of S and J.

Just as M^2 commutes with M_x, M_y and M_z, S^2 and J^2 also commute with their components, but the components of M^2 and S^2 do not commute with either J^2 or its components (except for like components).

We can therefore select from among the angular momentum operators various sets which commute among themselves and also with the Hamiltonian. The two alternatives are M^2, M_z, S^2, S_z and J_z or M^2, S^2,

J^2 and J_z. We can choose our eigenfunctions of the Hamiltonian so that they are also eigenfunctions of one of these sets of operators. When this is done the matrix component of H between eigenfunctions which have different eigenvalues for any one of these operators will vanish. An important consequence of this leads to factorization of the secular determinant. If we construct linear combinations of our basis functions, such that they fall into sets with identical values for one or other of the sets of operators, the element of the Hamiltonian between functions falling into different sets will vanish.

By suitable rearrangement of the rows and columns of the determinant, the secular determinant reduces to block diagonal form, and is then factored into several small determinants which can be handled with much less difficulty.

5. Other Methods of Obtaining Ground State Functions

The self-consistent field method given above is not the only way in which a best atomic wave function can be calculated. Another method is to allow excited configurations to interact with the ground state. We write down Slater determinants in which some electrons are excited to higher orbitals. For example

$$\begin{aligned}\Psi_A = |\psi_1(1)\,\alpha(1)\,\psi_1(2)\,\beta(2)\ldots\psi_{(N/2)-1}(N-3)\,\alpha(N-3)\,\psi_{(N/2)-1}(N-2)\\ \beta(N-2)\,\psi_{(N/2)+1}(N-1)\,\alpha(N-1)\,\psi_{(N/2)+1}(N)\,\beta(N)| \qquad (27)\end{aligned}$$

in which two electrons have been promoted from $\psi_{N/2}$ to $\psi_{(N/2)+1}$. Another example would be

$$\Psi_J = |\psi_1(1)\,\alpha(1)\,\psi_1(2)\,\beta(2)\ldots\psi_{N/2}(N-1)\,\alpha(N-1)\,\psi_{(N/2)+1}(N)\,\beta(N)| \qquad (28)$$

in which one electron has been excited from $\psi_{N/2}$ to $\psi_{(N/2)+1}$. Writing down other determinants $\Psi_B, \Psi_C\ldots\Psi_K, \Psi_L\ldots$ in a similar way we can form a linear variation function

$$\Phi = C_0\,\Psi_0 + C_A\,\Psi_A\ldots C_J\,\Psi_J\ldots C_M\,\Psi_M \qquad (29)$$

This is tantamount to writing down our ground state as an expansion of the complete set of functions. The set of Slater determinants do in fact form a complete set of $(M+1)$ orthonormal functions.

Forming

$$\int \Phi^*\,h\Phi d\tau$$

and setting

$$\frac{\partial E}{\partial C_i} = 0 \quad (i = 0, A, B, C\ldots M)$$

we are led to $(M+1)$ simultaneous equations

$$\sum_N (H_{MN}-S_{MN}E)C_N = 0 \quad (M = 0, A, B, C \ldots M) \tag{31}$$

where the matrix elements H_{MN} and S_{MN} (which will usually be diagonal) have the form

$$H_{MN} = \int \Psi_M^* H \Psi_N \, d\tau \tag{32}$$

$$S_{MN} = \int \Psi_M^* \Psi_N \, d\tau \tag{33}$$

There will be matrix elements H_{MN} and S_{MN} only if Ψ_M and Ψ_N have the same symmetry (Condon & Shortley (1934), Chapter 15); this amounts to their having the same eigenvalues of the operators of angular momentum, as discussed in the last section, which commute with the Hamiltonian.

The only non-trivial solutions of (31) occur when the determinant

$$|H_{MN}-S_{MN}E| = 0 \tag{34}$$

The lowest eigenvalue of this determinant is an upper bound to the true ground state energy (McDonald, 1933). The coefficients C_M can then be determined by substitution of the ground state eigenvalue into (31) plus the requirement that the wave function be normalized. The higher eigenvalues similarly give upper bounds to the energies of the excited states.

If we confine our linear variation function to determinants in which only one electron has been excited from the ground state, the resultant ground state, after configuration interaction, is equivalent to the self-consistent ground state (Brillouin, 1934).

A further consequence of Brillouin's theorem is that all one-electron operators are diagonalized when self-consistent field orbitals are used as a basis for the calculation.

6. Excited Atomic States

Consider an N-electron atom whose wave function for the ground state is given by equation (6). Let us excite an electron from orbital j to orbital l. There are different ways of doing this, depending upon whether we excite the electron with α spin or β spin. The two determinants which arise are

$$\left.\begin{aligned} \Phi_A &= |\psi_1(1)\,\alpha(1)\,\psi_1(2)\,\beta(2)\ldots\psi_j(N)\,\alpha(N) \\ &\qquad \psi_{N/2}(N-1)\,\alpha(N-1)\,\psi_{N/2}(N)\,\beta(N)\,\psi_l(L+1)\,\beta(L+1)| \\ \text{and} \quad & \\ \Phi_B &= |\psi_1(1)\,\alpha(1)\,\psi_1(2)\,\beta(2)\ldots\psi_j(L)\,\beta(L) \\ &\qquad \psi_{N/2}(N-1)\,\alpha(N-1)\,\psi_{N/2}(N)\,\beta(N)\,\psi_l(L+1)\,\alpha(L+1)| \end{aligned}\right\} \tag{35}$$

We find that the two configurations in which the singly-occupied orbitals have parallel spins must also be included; these are

$$\left.\begin{aligned}\Phi_C &= |\psi_1(1)\,\alpha(1)\,\psi_1(2)\,\beta(2)\ldots\psi_j(L)\,\alpha(L)\ldots\psi_l(L+1)\,\alpha(L+1)|\\ \Phi_D &= |\psi_1(1)\,\alpha(1)\,\psi_1(2)\,\beta(2)\ldots\psi_j(L)\,\beta(L)\ldots\psi_l(L+1)\,\beta(L+1)|\end{aligned}\right\} \tag{36}$$

From these four wave functions we find that one has an eigenvalue of S_z or $+0$ and the other three have eigenvalues of $1, 0, -1$. The states which arise from a single electron excitation from a singlet ground state are therefore a singlet and a triplet. The wave functions for these states are

$$^1\Phi_{j\to l} = \frac{1}{\sqrt{2}}(A-B) \tag{37}$$

for the singlet, and

$$^3\Phi_{j\to l}\left\{\begin{matrix}\frac{1}{\sqrt{2}}(A+B)\\ C\\ D\end{matrix}\right\} \tag{38}$$

for the triplet.

The energy expressions for these excited states are well known (see, for example, Condon & Shortley, 1934) and are given by

$$\begin{aligned}^{1,3}E_{j\to l} = {} & 2\sum_i f_i+f_j+f_l+\sum_{h,i}(2J_{hi}-K_{hi})+\sum_i(2J_{ij}-K_{ij})+\\ & +\sum_i(2J_{il}-K_{il})+J_{jl}+K_{jl}\end{aligned} \tag{39}$$

where we take the + sign for the singlet and the − sign for the triplet. The summations are taken over the orbitals occupied in the ground state. The f, J and K are defined as in (8). The energy of the orbitals j and l (ground and excited state orbitals respectively) are given by (following (13))

$$\left.\begin{aligned}\epsilon_j &= f_j+\sum_i(2J_{ij}+K_{ij})\\ \text{and}\qquad & \\ \epsilon_l &= f_l+\sum_i(2J_{il}-K_{il})\end{aligned}\right\} \tag{40}$$

where the summations are carried out over all of the occupied orbitals in the ground state.

Using these definitions (39) becomes

$$^{1,3}E_{j\to l} = \text{inner shell energy}+\epsilon_j+\epsilon_l-J_{jl}+K_{jl}\pm K_{jl} \tag{41}$$

The transition energy which we obtain by subtracting the energy of the ground state (8) from (41) is

$$^{1,3}E_{j\to l}-E_0 = \epsilon_l-\epsilon_j-J_{jl}+K_{jl}\pm K_{jl} \tag{42}$$

We see from equation (42) that a transition energy is not just a simple difference in orbital energies, but includes certain two-electron terms also.

Consider the case in which two electrons have been excited from orbital ψ_j to ψ_l. Our excited state differs from the ground state in that one orbital which was doubly occupied is now completely empty, and these electrons have now been placed in an orbital with higher energy. We can approximate our wave function by the one-determinant function

$$\begin{aligned} \Phi_{j^2\to l^2} = {} & |\psi_1(1)\,\alpha(1)\,\psi_1(2)\,\beta(2)\ldots\psi_{N/2}(N-1)\,\alpha(N-1) \\ & \psi_{N/2}(N)\,\beta(N)\,\psi_l(L)\,\alpha(L)\,\psi_l(L+1)\,\beta(L+1)| \end{aligned} \tag{43}$$

The energy of this configuration follows immediately from (8) and is given by

$$E_{jj\to ll} = 2f_i + 2f_l + \sum_{gh} (2J_{gh} - K_{gh}) + 2\sum_{g} (2J_{gl} - K_{gl}) + J_{ll} \tag{44}$$

where the summations are carried out over all of the ground state orbitals except j. The energy of the excited configuration with respect to the ground state (the transition energy) is then given by

$$E_{jj\to ll} - E_0 = 2\epsilon_l - 2\epsilon_j + J_{ll} \tag{45}$$

These transitions are not however the energies of the corresponding excited states. This arises because the basis orbitals which we have used to construct the wave functions of the excited configurations are not the "best" orbitals for the excited state problem. They are the "best" orbitals for the ground state, i.e. they are self-consistent field orbitals. If we want "best" one-electron orbitals for the excited state then we must solve the appropriate self-consistent field problem.

In order to obtain the "best" excited state wave function we must write variation functions in which we include all desired one-determinant functions of the correct multiplicity. We then carry out the normal variation calculation and find excited state wave functions which are linear combinations of Slater determinants.

The off-diagonal elements of the configuration interaction determinant have the following form

$$\left.\begin{aligned} ({}^1\Phi_{i\to k}|h|\,{}^1\Phi_{j\to l}) &= -J_{ik,jl} + 2K_{ik,il} \\ ({}^1\Phi_{i\to k}|h|\,{}^1\Phi_{i\to l}) &= \epsilon_{kl} - J_{ik,il} + 2K_{ik,il} \\ ({}^1\Phi_{i\to k}|h|\,{}^1\Phi_{j\to k}) &= \epsilon_{ij} - J_{ik,jk} + 2K_{ik,jk} \end{aligned}\right\} \tag{46}$$

These last two types of term disappear if ground state self-consistent field orbitals are used. If self-consistent field orbitals are not used, then there will be interaction elements between the ground state and singly-excited singlet configurations.

$$\left.\begin{array}{lr}\text{(i)} & (\Phi_0|h|\,^1\Phi_{i\to k}) = 2^{\frac{1}{2}}\,\epsilon_{ik} \\ \text{(ii)} & (\Phi_0|h|\,^1\Phi_{jj\to ll}) = 4J_{jl}-2K_{jl}\end{array}\right\} \quad (47)$$

Similar expressions hold for the interaction between triplet excited states.

7. Molecular Orbital Theory

In molecular theory, even in the simplest case of the hydrogen molecule ion, approximate methods must always be employed to solve the wave equation.

One approximation, that of molecular orbitals, runs exactly parallel to the theory of many-electron atoms, except that the one-electron orbitals are polycentric and not monocentric as in the atomic case. The N-electrons are assigned two at a time to molecular orbitals which may be chosen to be one-electron orbitals obtained by solving the problem ignoring electron interactions, and also by ignoring the movement of the nuclei (Born & Oppenheimer (1927)). Calling the one-electron functions $\psi_1, \psi_2, \psi_3 \ldots$, a wave function satisfying the problem without electron interaction is

$$\Psi = \psi_1.\psi_2.\psi_3\ldots\psi_N \quad (48)$$

This solution is unsatisfactory for the same reasons as was (5) unacceptable and must be replaced by a Slater determinant. When electron interaction is admitted the single determinant may remain a good approximation if the ψ's are allowed to vary and are properly chosen. A flexible and useful form of molecular orbital is a linear combination of atomic orbitals such as

$$\psi = \sum_i c_i \phi_i \quad (49)$$

where the ϕ_i are atomic orbitals belonging to the constituent atoms of the molecule. Such orbitals, constructed from a finite set of AOs are essentially approximate solutions of a one-electron problem; they are usually referred to as LCAO MOs.

The necessary molecular self-consistent field theory which leads to the equations determining the best one-electron orbitals (LCAO MOs) was first developed by Roothaan (1951). Assuming the ϕ's to be orthonormal, use of (49) in (15) yields a set of linear equations for the best values of the coefficients which may be written in matrix form as

$$\mathbf{h}^F\mathbf{T} = \mathbf{T}\boldsymbol{\epsilon} \quad (50)$$

where **T** is an $n \times n$ matrix whose columns are the AO coefficients (49). Operation of $\mathbf{h}^F$ on each column of **T** leads to a set of simultaneous equations

$$\mathbf{h}^F T_A = \epsilon_A T_A \tag{51}$$

The matrix elements $\mathbf{h}^F_{ij}$ are given by

$$h^F_{ij} = \int \phi_i^* h^F \phi_j dv \tag{52}$$

In the SCF theory these elements are determined semi-empirically or are calculated in terms of the charge density, whereas in the crude theory they are independent of the charge density and may only be determined empirically. The matrix $\boldsymbol{\epsilon}$ is the matrix of eigenvalues, or orbital energies, corresponding to the columns of **T**. These are determined by solution of the determinant

$$|h_F - \epsilon| = 0 \tag{53}$$

Substitution of the eigenvalues into (51) gives the columns of **T**.

Either the crude or SCF one-electron orbitals may be used as a basis for a configuration interaction calculation, in which several Slater determinants are allowed to mix as previously discussed.

References

Born, M. & Oppenheimer, J. R. (1927). *Annln Phys.* **84**, 457.
Brillouin, L. (1934). *Actual. scient. ind.*, No. 159.
Condon, E. V. & Shortley, G. H. (1934). "Theory of Atomic Spectra." Cambridge University Press.
McDonald, J. K. L. (1933). *Phys. Rev.* **43**, 880.
Roothaan, C. C. J. (1951). *Rev. Mod. Phys.* **23**, 69.
Slater, J. C. (1929). *Phys. Rev.* **34**, 1293.
Slater, J. C. (1930). *Phys. Rev.* **35**, 210.

CHAPTER 2

Molecular Orbital Theory

1. The Hückel Approximation

In the molecular orbital theory of π-electron compounds (e.g. conjugated hydrocarbons) (Hückel, 1931), the π-electrons are allocated one at a time to molecular orbitals which extend over all of the molecule. For a conjugated hydrocarbon with n carbon atoms there are $4n$ valence electrons. $3n$ of these are allocated to sp_2 hybrid orbitals to form $3n/2$ σ-bonds between the carbon atoms, these may be considered to be localized between each pair of atoms. Over this firmly bonded σ-electron framework the π-electrons move. All of the π-orbitals have a nodal plane in the plane of the nuclei. If the nuclear framework was expanded into an infinite sheet so that each carbon atom stayed in its hybrid valence state while all carbon–carbon bond distances became infinitely large, the orbitals would retain their characteristic symmetry properties but interaction between electrons would diminish. In the limit each carbon would have one π-electron in an orbital of the usual p type. For this reason orbitals for a conjugated system can be fairly well expressed as linear combinations of these $2p$ atomic orbitals. If we denote the p-orbital of the rth atom by ϕ_r then the molecular orbital (MO) ψ_J is written

$$\psi_J = \sum_r c_{rJ}\,\phi_r \quad (J = 1, 2, 3 \ldots n) \tag{1}$$

Taking this as a linear variation function, the coefficients may be determined using the variation principle. We seek stationary values of the integral

$$\frac{\int \psi_J^*\, h\psi_J\, d\tau}{\int \psi_J^*\, \psi_J\, d\tau} \tag{2}$$

where h is the "effective" Hamiltonian (of Chapter 1) (and must be defined ultimately on the basis of the Hartree–Fock theory), here considered to be independent of the actual electron distribution. This leads to the set of n simultaneous equations

$$\sum_s (h_{rs} - S_{rs} E)\, c_s = 0 \quad (r = 1, 2 \ldots n) \tag{3}$$

having solutions $\psi_1, \psi_B \ldots$ with corresponding sets of coefficients $c_{s1}, c_{s2} \ldots c_{sN}$; the eigenvalues follow from

$$|h_{rs} - S_{rs}E| = 0 \tag{4}$$

which, being an $n \times n$ determinant, has n eigenvalues; substitution of E_J into (3), together with the requirement that the wave function be normalized, gives the coefficients $c_{1J}, c_{2J} \ldots c_{nJ}$. These define the Jth molecular orbital. If we choose our set of basis functions ϕ to be orthonormal the terms in S_{rs} occur only along the diagonal. It is useful to do this although the restriction has been removed (Chirgwin & Coulson, 1950; McWeeny, 1959). Assuming orthonormal basis orbitals the MOs which result from (4) are also orthogonal in the sense

$$\sum_r \phi^*_{rA} \phi_{rB} = 0$$

J, K are also normalized to unity

$$\left(\sum_r \phi^*_{rA} \phi_{rA} = 1\right)$$

These properties are expressed by $\mathbf{c}^\dagger \mathbf{c} = \mathbf{c}\mathbf{c}^\dagger = \mathbf{1}$, where $\mathbf{c}$ is a square matrix whose rjth element is given by c_{rJ} and $\mathbf{1}$ is the unit matrix.

In the usual Hückel theory the matrix elements h_{rs} $(r \neq s)$ are regarded as negligible except for nearest neighbours, in which case they are given the value β. The elements h_{rr} are all given the same value α. The α, usually called the "Coulomb integral", and the β, usually called the

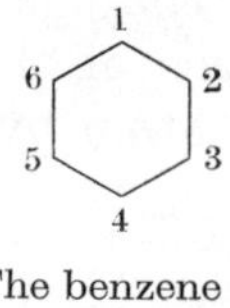

FIG. 1. The benzene molecule.

"resonance integral", are determined by appeal to experiment; they are both negative in absolute units. These assumptions imply that different bonds and different atoms are equivalent. This is, of course, only true to first order, and we shall see later that in the self-consistent field theory both α and β are dependent on the charges and bond orders.

We shall now calculate the orbital energies and orbital coefficients for benzene. The Hamiltonian matrix, $\mathbf{h}$, is

$$\begin{pmatrix} \alpha & \beta & 0 & 0 & 0 & \beta \\ \beta & \alpha & \beta & 0 & 0 & 0 \\ 0 & \beta & \alpha & \beta & 0 & 0 \\ 0 & 0 & \beta & \alpha & \beta & 0 \\ 0 & 0 & 0 & \beta & \alpha & \beta \\ \beta & 0 & 0 & 0 & \beta & \alpha \end{pmatrix}$$

The corresponding secular determinant is

$$\begin{vmatrix} \alpha-E & \beta & 0 & 0 & 0 & \beta \\ \beta & \alpha-E & \beta & 0 & 0 & 0 \\ 0 & \beta & \alpha-E & \beta & 0 & 0 \\ 0 & 0 & \beta & \alpha-E & \beta & 0 \\ 0 & 0 & 0 & \beta & \alpha-E & \beta \\ \beta & 0 & 0 & 0 & \beta & \alpha-E \end{vmatrix} = 0$$

It is a computational convenience to divide through by β and write $(\alpha-E)/\beta = -x$, so that x is the energy in units of β, above a reference level α, and in this case we have

$$\begin{vmatrix} -x & 1 & 0 & 0 & 0 & 1 \\ 1 & -x & 1 & 0 & 0 & 0 \\ 0 & 1 & -x & 1 & 0 & 0 \\ 0 & 0 & 1 & -x & 1 & 0 \\ 0 & 0 & 0 & 1 & -x & 1 \\ 1 & 0 & 0 & 0 & 1 & -x \end{vmatrix} = 0$$

This determinant may then be expanded and solved for x. The orbital energies are found to be $\alpha \pm 2\beta$ and $\alpha \pm \beta$ (twice), making six roots in all. Substitution of these values for the orbital energies in turn into the secular equations lead to the following set of coefficients:

$$\begin{array}{ll} \alpha+2\beta & \psi_1 = 6^{-1/2}(\phi_1+\phi_2+\phi_3+\phi_4+\phi_5+\phi_6) \\ \alpha+\beta & \begin{cases} \psi_2 = 12^{-1/2}(2\phi_1+\phi_2-\phi_3-2\phi_4-\phi_5+\phi_6) \\ \psi_3 = \frac{1}{2}(\phi_2+\phi_3-\phi_5-\phi_6) \end{cases} \\ \alpha-\beta & \begin{cases} \psi_4 = \frac{1}{2}(-\phi_2+\phi_3-\phi_5+\phi_6) \\ \psi_5 = 12^{-1/2}(2\phi_1-\phi_2-\phi_3+2\phi_4-\phi_5-\phi_6) \end{cases} \\ \alpha-2\beta & \psi_6 = 6^{-1/2}(\phi_1-\phi_2+\phi_3-\phi_4+\phi_5-\phi_6) \end{array}$$

So far we have adopted the crude one-electron model of simple MO theory, each electron being considered independently of the others. More properly we should use a Slater determinantal wave function (as discussed in Chapter 1). The lowest state, or ground state, occurs when the lowest $n/2$ orbitals are each doubly occupied (one electron with spin $+\frac{1}{2}$ and one with spin $-\frac{1}{2}$), in most of what follows only the case of n even is considered; we are concerned with the usual case of singlet ground states. For this state the simple theory takes the total energy to be

$$E = 2\sum_J E_J \quad (J \text{ runs over the } N/2 \text{ orbitals of lowest energy}) \qquad (6)$$

Obviously this is a poor approximation as electron interaction has not been properly included; its inclusion leads to a more complete energy expression and will be discussed in Chapter 5.

2. The Electron Density Distribution

The physical significance of the coefficients c_{rJ} of equation (1) is readily found. The probability density at any point r in space due to an electron in molecular orbital J is given by $\psi_J^*(r)\psi_J(r)$. The total density, with doubly occupied orbitals is then

$$P(1) = 2\sum_J \psi_J^*(r)\psi_J(r)$$

and

$$P(1) = \sum_r P_{rr}\phi_r^*\phi_r + \sum_{r,s} P_{rs}\phi_r^*\phi_s \tag{7}$$

where

$$P_{rr} = 2\sum_J c_{rJ}c_{rJ} \quad \text{and} \quad P_{rs} = 2\sum_J c_{rJ}c_{sJ}$$

P_{rr} is known as the π-charge density on atom r, while P_{rs} is the bond order of the bond r—s and largely determines the distribution of charge in the space between atoms r and s. The significance of the charges and bond orders was first discussed by Coulson (1939) and further by Coulson & Longuet-Higgins (1947), we shall have cause to refer to these quantities continually in what follows.

3. Alternant Hydrocarbons

An important class of hydrocarbons known as alternants was first discussed by Coulson & Rushbrooke (1940). If we consider the molecule

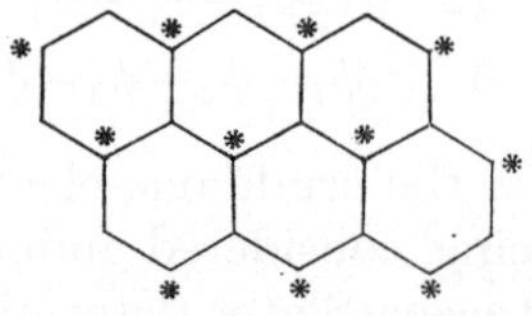

FIG. 2. An alternant hydrocarbon.

then commencing at any atom and starring every alternate atom, we find that irrespective of where we start, the atoms always fall into the same two groups, every atom being surrounded only by atoms of the other group. All molecules which possess this property are known as alternants.

Alternants which contain an even number of carbon atoms have several interesting properties which were pointed out by Coulson and Rushbrooke:

(1) The eigenvalues (orbital energies) of the secular determinant are symmetrically placed about α, i.e. if $\alpha+\beta$ is an eigenvalue then $\alpha-\beta$ is also. Every bonding orbital has an antibonding partner.
(2) If the coefficients of a bonding orbital are $a_1, a_2 \ldots$ and $b_1, b_2 \ldots$, a_i and b_i being the coefficients of the starred and unstarred sets, then the coefficients of the antibonding partner are $a_1, a_2 \ldots$ and $-b_1, -b_2 \ldots$.
(3) If each atom contributes one π-electron to the system then the charge distribution is uniform, each P_{ii} has the value unity.
(4) Bond orders between atoms of the same set are zero.

All of these points may be seen from an examination of the orbital energies and coefficients for benzene given above.

4. Heterocyclics

The simple theory can also be extended to a hetero-substituted molecule, e.g. pyridine, quinoline, etc. In these molecules the nitrogen atom replaces a C—H group in the ring and the number of π-electrons remains unchanged. In making such a substitution it is necessary to revise the values of α and β. In the case of α, the Coulomb integral is replaced by $\alpha+\beta\delta$ in order to describe the difference in electronegativity between the substituent atom and the displaced carbon atom. The value of δ is chosen to fit experimental data. For nitrogen, the values assumed vary between 2·0 in the older work to 0·5 in the more recent work; however, it is important to note that all values used have the same sign. Wheland & Pauling (1935) also introduced the technique of sharing the δ over the nearest neighbours, but self-consistent field theory shows that this practice is unsatisfactory (McWeeny, 1956a,b; McWeeny & Peacock, 1957). The β's for C—N and N—N bonds are usually taken to be the same as for C—C bonds.

5. Examples

We shall now calculate the orbital energies, orbital coefficients, charges and bond orders for some selected hydrocarbons.

(i) *Ethylene*. The ethylene molecule is shown diagrammatically in Fig. 3 together with the numbering of the atoms.

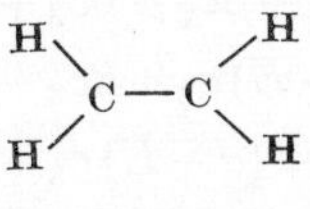

FIG. 3. The ethylene molecule.

The Hamiltonian is

$$h = \begin{pmatrix} \alpha & \beta \\ \beta & \alpha \end{pmatrix}$$

The secular equations are then

$$(\alpha - E)\,c_1 + \beta c_2 = 0$$
$$\beta c_1 + (\alpha - E)\,c_2 = 0$$

and the secular determinant is

$$\begin{vmatrix} (\alpha - E) & \beta \\ \beta & (\alpha - E) \end{vmatrix} = \begin{vmatrix} -x & 1 \\ 1 & -x \end{vmatrix} = 0$$

i.e.

$$x^2 - 1 = 0$$
$$x = \pm 1$$

The orbital energies are therefore $\alpha + \beta$ and $\alpha - \beta$. Substituting these values of E into our simultaneous equations and normalizing the solutions we have, for $\alpha + \beta$,

$$\psi_1 = 2^{-1/2}(\phi_1 + \phi_2)$$

and for $\alpha - \beta$,

$$\psi_2 = 2^{-1/2}(\phi_1 - \phi_2).$$

In the ground state the two π-electrons will both be in ψ_1. The π-charges and bond orders are

$$P_{11} = 2(2^{-1/2})^2 = 1, \quad P_{22} = 1, \quad P_{12} = 2(2^{-1/2}.2^{-1/2}) = 1$$

(ii) *Butadiene*. The molecule is shown in Fig. 4.

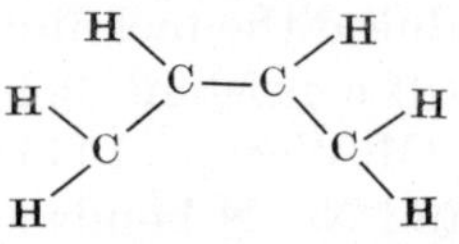

FIG. 4. The butadiene molecule.

The Hamiltonian is

$$h = \begin{pmatrix} \alpha & \beta & 0 & 0 \\ \beta & \alpha & \beta & 0 \\ 0 & \beta & \alpha & \beta \\ 0 & 0 & \beta & \alpha \end{pmatrix}$$

Our set of simultaneous equations are

$$(\alpha - E)\,c_1 + \beta c_2 + 0c_3 + 0c_4 = 0$$
$$\beta c_1 + (\alpha - E)\,c_2 + \beta c_3 + 0c_4 = 0$$
$$0c_1 + \beta c_2 + (\alpha - E)\,c_3 + \beta c_4 = 0$$
$$0c_1 + 0c_2 + \beta c_3 + (\alpha - E)\,c_4 = 0$$

The secular determinant is

$$\begin{vmatrix} -x & 1 & 0 & 0 \\ 1 & -x & 0 & 0 \\ 0 & 1 & -x & 1 \\ 0 & 0 & 1 & -x \end{vmatrix} = 0$$

leading to $x^4 - 3x^2 - 1 = 0$, which gives for the orbital energies $E_1 = \alpha + 1{\cdot}618\beta$, $E_2 = \alpha + 0{\cdot}618\beta$, $E_3 = \alpha - 0{\cdot}618\beta$, $E_4 = \alpha - 1{\cdot}618\beta$.

The corresponding orbitals are

$$\begin{aligned} \psi_1 &= 0{\cdot}3717\phi_1 + 0{\cdot}6015\phi_2 + 0{\cdot}6015\phi_3 + 0{\cdot}3717\phi_4 \\ \psi_2 &= 0{\cdot}6015\phi_1 + 0{\cdot}3717\phi_2 - 0{\cdot}3717\phi_3 - 0{\cdot}6015\phi_4 \\ \psi_3 &= 0{\cdot}6015\phi_1 - 0{\cdot}3717\phi_2 - 0{\cdot}3717\phi_3 + 0{\cdot}6015\phi_4 \\ \psi_4 &= 0{\cdot}3717\phi_1 - 0{\cdot}6015\phi_2 + 0{\cdot}6015\phi_3 - 0{\cdot}3717\phi_4 \end{aligned}$$

In the ground state ψ_1 and ψ_2 will both be doubly occupied. The π-charges and bond orders are:

$$P_{11} = P_{22} = P_{33} = P_{44} = 1, \quad P_{12} = P_{34} = 0{\cdot}894, \quad P_{23} = 0{\cdot}447$$

6. Symmetry Orbitals

Many conjugated molecules possess some symmetry elements and these may be used to reduce the size of the secular problem. We write linear combinations of the atomic orbitals which possess some symmetry properties of the molecule, then elements of **h** or **S** between functions possessing different symmetry properties disappear. These orbitals are called symmetry orbitals.

Consider butadiene; from Fig. 4 it can be seen that butadiene has a reflection plane through the mid-point of the bond 2—3 and perpendicular to it. Atoms 1 and 4 are obviously equivalent, as are atoms 2 and 3. We can then write

$$\begin{aligned} \bar{\phi}_1 &= 2^{-1/2}(\phi_1 + \phi_4) \\ \bar{\phi}_2 &= 2^{-1/2}(\phi_2 + \phi_3) \\ \bar{\phi}_3 &= 2^{-1/2}(\phi_2 - \phi_3) \\ \bar{\phi}_4 &= 2^{-1/2}(\phi_1 - \phi_4) \end{aligned}$$

$\bar{\phi}_1$ and $\bar{\phi}_2$ are symmetric with respect to reflection and $\bar{\phi}_3$ and $\bar{\phi}_4$ are antisymmetric with respect to reflection.

Evaluating the elements of h using these symmetry orbitals we have

$$\bar{h} = \begin{pmatrix} \alpha & \beta & 0 & 0 \\ \beta & \alpha+\beta & 0 & 0 \\ 0 & 0 & \alpha-\beta & \beta \\ 0 & 0 & \beta & \alpha \end{pmatrix}$$

$\bar{h}$ is then the Hamiltonian in the basis of the symmetry orbitals. The secular determinant is

$$\begin{vmatrix} -x & 1 & 0 & 0 \\ 1 & -x+1 & 0 & 0 \\ 0 & 0 & -x-1 & 1 \\ 0 & 0 & 1 & -x \end{vmatrix} = 0$$

which factorizes into

$$\begin{vmatrix} -x & 1 \\ 1 & -x+1 \end{vmatrix} = 0 \quad \text{and} \quad \begin{vmatrix} -x-1 & 1 \\ 1 & -x \end{vmatrix} = 0$$

which have roots 1·618 and $-0{\cdot}618$, and 0·618 and $-1{\cdot}618$ respectively. Substitution into the appropriate secular equations, viz.

$$\left.\begin{aligned} (\alpha-E)\bar{c}_1+\beta\bar{c}_2 &= 0 \\ \beta\bar{c}_1+(\alpha+\beta-E)\bar{c}_2 &= 0 \end{aligned}\right\}$$

and

$$\left.\begin{aligned} (\alpha-\beta-E)\bar{c}_3+\beta\bar{c}_4 &= 0 \\ \beta\bar{c}_3+(\alpha-E)\bar{c}_4 &= 0 \end{aligned}\right\}$$

together with the back transformation to ordinary atomic orbitals, yield the MOs given above in (5).

Secondly, consider naphthalene, which presents a 10×10 secular determinant if symmetry is not used. Naphthalene has two reflection planes perpendicular to the molecular plane—one marked a and the other marked b in Fig. 5.

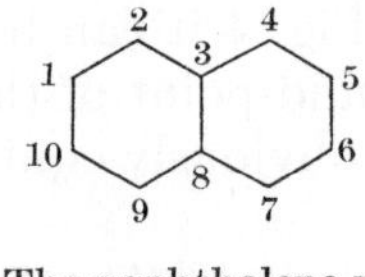

FIG. 5. The naphthalene molecule.

We can write four kinds of symmetry orbitals for naphthalene:

(i) Those symmetric with respect to a and b.

(ii) Those symmetric with respect to a but antisymmetric with respect to b.

(iii) Those antisymmetric with respect to a and symmetric with respect to b.

(iv) Those antisymmetric with respect to both a and b.

From Fig. 5 it can be seen that atoms 1, 5, 6 and 10 are equivalent; atoms 2, 4, 7 and 9 are equivalent; and atoms 3 and 8 form a third equivalent set.

Our symmetry orbitals for naphthalene are:

(i)
$$\bar{\phi}_1 = \tfrac{1}{2}(\phi_1+\phi_5+\phi_6+\phi_{10})$$
$$\bar{\phi}_2 = \tfrac{1}{2}(\phi_2+\phi_4+\phi_7+\phi_9)$$
$$\bar{\phi}_3 = 2^{-1/2}(\phi_3+\phi_8)$$

(ii)
$$\bar{\phi}_4 = \tfrac{1}{2}(\phi_2-\phi_4-\phi_7+\phi_9)$$
$$\bar{\phi}_5 = \tfrac{1}{2}(\phi_1-\phi_5-\phi_6+\phi_{10})$$

(iii)
$$\bar{\phi}_6 = \tfrac{1}{2}(\phi_1+\phi_5-\phi_6-\phi_{10})$$
$$\bar{\phi}_7 = \tfrac{1}{2}(\phi_2+\phi_4-\phi_7-\phi_9)$$
$$\bar{\phi}_8 = 2^{-1/2}(\phi_3-\phi_8)$$

(iv)
$$\bar{\phi}_9 = \tfrac{1}{2}(\phi_2-\phi_4+\phi_7-\phi_9)$$
$$\bar{\phi}_{10} = \tfrac{1}{2}(\phi_1-\phi_5+\phi_6-\phi_{10})$$

Use of these symmetry orbitals reduces the size of the secular determinant from one 10×10 to two 3×3 and two 1×1 determinants.

Even now when automatic computational facilities are in universal use, it is frequently convenient and certainly economic in storage space to work in symmetry orbitals.

The most efficient method of constructing symmetry orbitals is to use the irreducible representations of the appropriate point group. The combinations of the basis atomic orbitals which form bases for the irreducible representations can then be found in a straightforward manner. This method of obtaining symmetry orbitals is discussed in the appendix.

7. Bond Order and Bond Length

In Section 2 we defined a quantity which we called the π-bond order. According to equation (7), this quantity is defined by $2\sum_J c_{rJ}c_{sJ}$ for a bond r—s. Integration of the equation for (1) in (7) gives the total distribution of charge in the molecule. We have

$$\int P(1)\,dv = \sum_r \int P_{rr}\phi_r^*\phi_r\,dv + \sum_{r,s}\int P_{rs}\phi_r\phi_s\,dv$$
$$= \sum_r P_{rr}\int \phi_r^*\phi_s\,dv + \sum_{r,s} P_{rs}\int \phi_r^*\phi_s\,dv$$
$$= \sum_r P_{rr} + \sum_{rs} P_{rs}S_{rs} = N \qquad (8)$$

where N is the total number of π-electrons.

We see from (8) that the π-bond order is related to the amount of charge in the bond—i.e. to the delocalization of the electrons from the atoms. Since S_{rs}, the overlap integral, varies little between one conjugated bond and another, we can say that the bond order is a good measure of the π-electron density in the bond. From Section 3 we can make some further observations. In ethylene we see that the bond order has the value unity. This corresponds to a fixed double bond and is the highest possible value for a bond order in a molecule containing only double and single bonds. When we go to butadiene, which has four carbon atoms and four π-electrons, there is a different state of affairs. Butadiene may be considered as two ethylene molecules joined together by a carbon–carbon single bond to first approximation. In which case we should have two isolated double bonds each with a bond order unity and a single bond with π-order zero. The calculation which we did in Section 3 does not support this view, however. We find that the outer bonds have orders of 0·894 and the inner bond has an order of 0·447. In other words the "double" bonds are not pure isolated double bonds and the single bond has a certain amount of double bond character. This breaking away from alternating double and single bonds leads to a stabilization of the molecule which we shall discuss further in the next section. This delocalization of the charge in the π-bonds is called conjugation and molecules which possess alternating "double" and "single" bond character are called "conjugated molecules".

When we come to benzene we notice a further interesting fact. Using the orbitals given for the π-orbitals of benzene in Section 1, we find that the bond order of each bond in benzene has the value two-thirds. In other words, instead of alternating single and double bonds in benzene, as one would expect in terms of classical valence structures, we have six bonds which are all equivalent. Here then we have a maximum sharing or delocalization of the π-bond electrons.

As well as the π-bonds in these molecules we have also the σ-bonds which are formed from the electrons assigned to the sp_2 hybrid orbitals of the carbon. Following Coulson (1939) we can then define a total bond order

$$P_{rs} = P^{\sigma}_{rs} + P^{\pi}_{rs} \tag{9}$$

Since the σ-electrons are always considered to be localized we may write

$$P_{rs} = 1 + P^{\pi}_{rs} \tag{10}$$

In acetylene we have two π-bonds at right angles to each other, each with a bond order of unity. The total bond order here then will be three. In Table 1 we give the total bond orders for ethylene, butadiene, benzene and acetylene and show how these are made up from the π and σ parts.

TABLE 1. Bond orders for selected molecules

	Ethylene	Butadiene		Benzene	Acetylene
P^{π}_{rs}	1·000	0·894	0·447	0·667	2·000
P^{σ}_{rs}	1·000	1·000	1·000	1·000	1·000
P_{rs}	2·000	1·894	1·447	1·667	3·000

Since there is a connexion between π-bond order and double bond character we are entitled to ask if there is any relation between bond lengths and bond orders. Coulson (1939) did in fact derive such a relationship. He found that the relationship is

$$x = s - \frac{s-d}{1+k(1-P)/P} \tag{11}$$

where s is the length of a "natural" single bond, and d the length of a double bond. k is a parameter which must be determined by appeal to

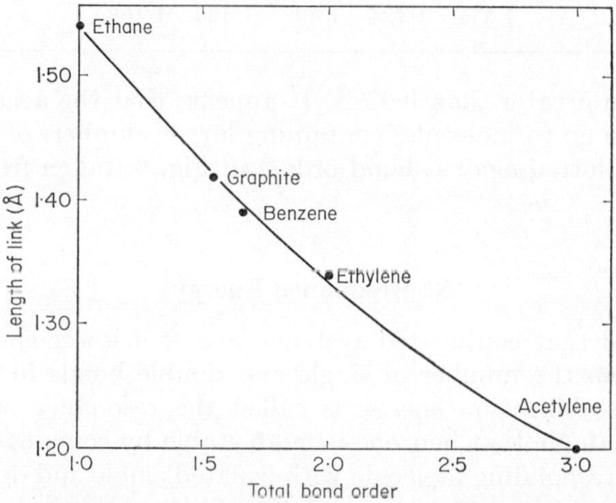

FIG. 6. Bond order plotted against bond length (Coulson, 1961). (By permission of the Oxford University Press.)

experiment. We can use the values of x, the bond length, and P for ethylene, benzene and graphite (where the bond order is found to be 0·535 and x to be 1·421 Å) to determine the values of the two unknowns s and k. These equations give us values of 1·515 Å for s and 1·05 Å for k. In Fig. 6 we show the relationship between the bond length and the π-bond order. Bond lengths predicted using this relationship agree fairly well with the experimental values of the bond lengths.

In Table 2 we give the predicted bond lengths and experimental lengths for naphthalene and anthracene (Pritchard & Sumner, 1955). In calculations for a wide range of molecules Coulson has found that in few cases is

TABLE 2. Bond lengths for naphthalene and anthracene

	Bond			
	1–2	2–3	3–8	1–10
Naphthalene				
Predicted (Å)	1·337	1·410	1·417	1·400
Experimental (Å)	1·365	1·425	1·393	1·404

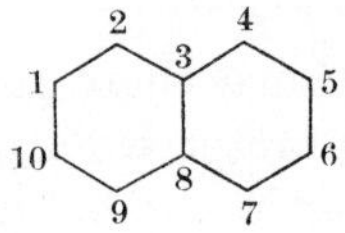

	Bond				
	1–2	2–3	3–4	3–12	1–14
Anthracene					
Predicted (Å)	1·375	1·414	1·400	1·424	1·404
Experimental (Å)	1·371	1·424	1·396	1·436	1·408

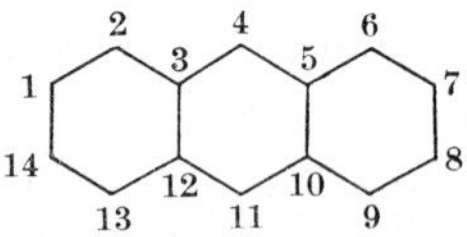

the deviation greater than 0·02 Å. It appears that the accuracy is improved as we go to molecules containing larger numbers of rings. Bond lengths are plotted against bond orders in Fig. 6 (taken from Coulson, 1961).

8. Resonance Energy

It is found that conjugated systems possess a lower energy than is expected from the number of single and double bonds in the system. This extra stabilization energy is called the resonance energy. It is found for example that benzene is more stable by some 64·4 kcal/mole than the corresponding molecule with isolated single and double bonds.

Looking once more at our calculation for benzene in Section 1, we find that the total energy of the molecule is $6\alpha + 8\beta$. If we isolated the double bonds the total π-electron energy would be $6\alpha + 6\beta$. The additional energy of 2β which occurs through delocalization of the double bonds is called the resonance energy or, more properly, the delocalization energy. More refined empirical estimates of the resonance energy give a value of 36 kcal/mole. We have then a method for the determination of the resonance integral β.

In Table 3 we give the calculated delocalization energies for some aromatic hydrocarbons and the corresponding values of the empirical

TABLE 3. Delocalization energies and resonance energies for some polyacenes

Hydrocarbon	Delocalization energy (β)	Resonance energy (kcal/mole)	$\frac{\text{R.E.}}{\text{D.E.}}$
Benzene	−2·000	36·0	18
Naphthalene	−3·683	61·0	16·6
Anthracene	−5·314	83·5	15·8
Tetracene	−6·932	110·0	15·9

resonance energies, in the fourth column we give the ratio resonance energy/delocalization energy. It can easily be seen that the values of β obtained in the four cases given, which are the first four members of a series of related molecules, do not give a consistent value of β, although the orders of magnitude are the same in all cases. This value of −16 kcal/mole is smaller than that obtained from other data. We shall discuss this point in greater detail later. Other things apart, the values of the empirical resonance energy are very sensitive to the method used in obtaining them. When we look at olefins and polyenes we find that the value obtained for β is −6 kcal. It is clear that there is no real agreement even on order of magnitude for β.

FIG. 7.

In deriving our theoretical estimate for the resonance energy, we have used a hypothetical reference molecule for benzene containing single and double bonds. This reference molecule will have different lengths for the single and double bonds. The structure we have assumed has the geometry of the conjugated molecule. The difference is shown diagrammatically in Fig. 7. In order to make the comparison more valid we must change our values of the bond energies for the single and double bonds to allow for compression of the single bonds and extension of the double bonds. The resonance energy thus derived is called a vertical resonance energy. Coulson & Altmann (1952) have estimated that the distortion energy for benzene amounts to some 27 kcal/mole. Since the molecule must overcome this energy and still give an empirical resonance energy of 36 kcal, the vertical resonance energy must be about 63 kcal. Mulliken & Parr (1951) have estimated the vertical resonance energy for benzene to be 73 kcal. Other estimates are as high as 117·5 kcal (Glockler, 1953).

One thing which emerges from this discussion is that resonance energies are not a very good method by which to determine the value of β. The various values for β obtained from vertical resonance energies range from 31·5 to 55·5 kcal.

Calculations of resonance energies have also been used to calculate the value of δ for nitrogen heterocyclic atoms. Using first-order perturbation theory it is readily seen from the benzene orbital coefficients given in Section 2, that the delocalization energy in pyridine is $-(2+\frac{1}{2}\delta)\beta$. By comparing the value of the empirical resonance energy for benzene and pyridine we can make an estimate of the value for δ. Wheland & Pauling (1935) obtained a value of 2·0 for δ in this way. In view of the assumptions made in calculating vertical resonance energies it is clear that such values of δ are unreliable.

9. Ionization Potentials

The total energy of a molecule in its ground state, where the lowest $n/2$ molecular orbitals are all doubly occupied is

$$E = 2\sum_{J} E_J \quad (J \text{ occupied}) \tag{12}$$

When one electron is removed from the system, the topmost orbital, say Ψ_k, will only be singly occupied, and the total π-electron energy will then be

$$E^{+} = 2\sum_{J}{}' E_J + E_K \quad (\text{summation does not include } E_K) \tag{13}$$

The difference between the energy of the molecule and the ion will be the energy required to ionize an electron from the molecule. This energy is called the ionization potential. It follows from (12) and (13) that I, the ionization potential, is given by

$$I = E^{+} - E = -E_K \tag{14}$$

The identification of the ionization potential with the negative of the highest orbital energy is known as Koopmans' theorem (1933) and is rigorously true in the theory of solids.

Values for the ionization potential permit us to make an estimate of both α and β. The value of α may be obtained from a knowledge of the π ionization potential for graphite. The experimental value is 4·3 eV. Since the energy of the topmost orbital in graphite is α, the value of α is $-4{\cdot}3$ eV.

In Table 4 we give the values of the ionization potential for the first four members of the polyacene series as determined by electron impact and ultra-violet spectroscopy. The energy of the topmost orbital is also given.

TABLE 4

	Ionization potential		
	E.I.	U.V.	Orbital energy
Benzene	9·57	9·245	$\alpha+1{\cdot}000\beta$
Naphthalene	8·68	8·12	$\alpha+0{\cdot}618\beta$
Anthracene	8·20		$\alpha+0{\cdot}414\beta$
Tetracene	7·71		$\alpha+0{\cdot}295\beta$

Using our value of α from graphite we obtain values of β of about 7 eV, with a very wide scatter. Eliminating α from consideration and obtaining β values by plotting ionization potential against energy and taking the slope, we find a value for β of about $-2{\cdot}4$ eV, i.e. -55 kcal/mole. It is clear that ionization potential data is unable to give us either a reliable value of α or a value of β which is comparable to that obtained from resonance energy data. When we come to consider radicals and second ionization potentials it is seen that there is no correlation at all between ionization potentials and the Hückel α and β.

The main reason for the disagreement between theory and experiment and the general inadequacy of the Hückel model is the neglect of interaction between the π-electrons. We shall see in a later chapter how these interactions may be included in our model.

It would appear that ionization potentials could be used to determine the value of δ for heterocyclic atoms. It has been found by the present author that there is no correlation between the topmost orbital energies and the ionization potentials for pyridine, pyridazine, pyrimidinc and pyrazine (McWeeny & Peacock, 1957).

10. Dipole Moments

The dipole moment of a molecule is given by

$$\mu = e\int \psi^* r\psi\, dv$$

$$\mu = e\left\{\left(\int \psi^* x\psi\, dv + \int \psi^* y\psi\, dv + \int \psi^* z\psi\, dv\right)\right\} \tag{15}$$

The dipole moments which arise from the π-electrons in conjugated molecules may be evaluated readily from the vector addition of the bond moments. We make here the well-established assumption that the bond moments are relatively constant constitutive properties of the σ-bonds of compounds. Our total dipole moment then becomes

$$\mu = \mu^\sigma + \mu^\pi \tag{16}$$

It remains to evaluate the π contribution to the moment. The π-electron wave function may be written

$$\psi = \psi_A(1)\alpha(1)\psi_A(2)\beta(2)\ldots\psi_{N/2}(N)\beta(N) \tag{17}$$

Each molecular orbital ψ_J may be expanded in terms of the linear combination of atomic orbitals (1). Since the dipole moment operator is a one-electron operator we obtain

$$\mu = e2\sum_J \int \psi_J^* r\psi_J\,dv = e2\sum_J\sum_{rs} c_r^* c_s \int \phi_r^* r\phi_s\,dv \tag{18}$$

We now divide and multiply each term by the integral $\int \psi_J^* \psi_J dv = S_{rs}$.

$$\mu = e\left(\sum_r P_{rr}\frac{\int \phi_r^* r\phi_s\,dv}{\int \phi_r^* \phi_r\,dv}dv \times \int \phi_r^* \phi_s dv + \sum_{rs} P_{rs}\frac{\int \phi_r^* r\phi_s\,dv}{\int \phi_r^* \phi_s\,dv}\int \phi_r^* \phi_s\,dv\right) \tag{19}$$

The first half of each term then becomes the respective component of the centroid of the atomic orbital r or the bond r—s as the case may be and the second half on overlap integral. The equation for the dipole moment then takes the very simple form

$$\left.\begin{aligned} \mu_x &= e\left(\sum_r P_{rr}\,X_r + \sum_{rs} P_{rs}\,X_{rs}S_{rs}\right) \\ \mu_y &= e\left(\sum_r P_{rr}\,Y_r + \sum_{rs} P_{rs}\,Y_{rs}S_{rs}\right) \\ \mu_z &= e\left(\sum_r P_{rr}\,Z_r + \sum_r P_{rs}\,Z_{rs}S_{rs}\right) \end{aligned}\right\} \tag{20}$$

and

$$\mu^2 = \mu_x^2 + \mu_y^2 + \mu_z^2$$

and the magnitude of the π-dipole moment is then

$$|\mu| = (\mu_x^2 + \mu_y^2 + \mu_z^2)^{1/2} \tag{21}$$

We must calculate then the dipole moment which arises from the ionic framework over which the π-electrons move. This is given simply by

$$\left.\begin{aligned} \mu_x^I &= \sum_r Z_r X_r \\ \mu_y^I &= \sum_r Z_r Y_r \\ \mu_z^I &= \sum_r Z_r Z_r \end{aligned}\right\} \tag{22}$$

The total dipole moment will then have components

$$\mu_x^\pi = \mu_x + \mu_x^I$$

$$\mu_y^\pi = \mu_y + \mu_y^I \tag{23}$$

$$\mu_z^\pi = \mu_z + \mu_z^I \tag{24}$$

The centroids of the orbitals are usually located at the nuclei for the atom charges and the bond mid-points for the bonds. An alternative expression for the dipole moment is given in terms of the net π-electron charge in atoms and bonds. We write

$$q_r = (P_{rr} - Z_r) \tag{25}$$

and

$$q_{rs} = 2P_{rs}S_{rs} \tag{26}$$

Equations (23) then have the form

$$\left.\begin{aligned} \mu_x^\pi &= \sum_r q_r X_r + \sum_{rs} q_{rs} X_{rs} \\ \mu_y^\pi &= \sum_r q_r Y_r + \sum_{rs} q_{rs} Y_{rs} \quad \text{(each bond is counted only once)} \\ \mu_z^\pi &= \sum_r q_r Z_r + \sum_{rs} q_{rs} Z_{rs} \end{aligned}\right\} \tag{27}$$

and

$$\mu^\pi = (\mu_x^2 + \mu_y^2 + \mu_z^2)^{1/2} \tag{28}$$

Alternant hydrocarbons do not possess π-dipole moments although they may possess a small σ-moment. Non-alternant hydrocarbons and heterocyclics may, however, possess a dipole moment.

In writing the co-ordinates of the atom and bond centroids we usually treat them as vectors with some fixed point, usually the mass centroid of the molecule, as the origin.

Dipole moments have been used to determine the value of δ for heterocyclic atoms. The method gives values of δ which lie around 0·5. Davies (1955) calculated the dipole moments for the series pyridine, pyridazine, pyrimidine, pyrazine, using a value of $\delta = 0{\cdot}58$. He did two series of calculations, one with inclusion of overlap and the other assuming a basis of orthogonalized $2p_z$-orbitals. His results are given in Table 5.

TABLE 5. Dipole moments for the azines

	With overlap (D)	Without overlap (D)	Expt. (D)
Pyridine	2·25	2·30	2·2
Pyridazine	3·60	3·69	3·9
Pyrimidine	2·24	2·26	2·4
Pyrazine			

We shall take up later the reasons for the discrepancy between the values in orthogonalized orbitals and the values obtained using non-orthogonal orbitals.

Similar work on oxygen-substituted heterocyclics has given a value of 1·0 for δ in situations where oxygen contributes one electron to the δ-shell (see, for example, Perez, Herraez, Igea & Esteve (1955)).

We shall now calculate the π-dipole moment for pyridine, using the charge distribution given by Coulson (1961, p. 258), assuming a δ value of 0·5. This charge distribution is shown in Fig. 8. The values of q are

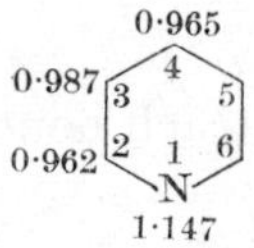

FIG. 8. Charge distribution in pyridine.

$q_1 = +0{\cdot}147$, $q_2 = -0{\cdot}038$, $q_3 = -0{\cdot}013$ and $q_4 = -0{\cdot}035$. The co-ordinates of the atoms, referred to the centre of the molecule, are 1 $(0, -1)$, 2 $(-\sqrt{3}/2, -\frac{1}{2})$, 3 $(-\sqrt{3}/2, \frac{1}{2})$, 4 $(0, 1)$, 5 $(\sqrt{3}/2, \frac{1}{2})$ and 6 $(\sqrt{3}/2, -\frac{1}{2})$. The co-ordinates are given in terms of the bond length, 1·40 Å. The x-component of the dipole moment is zero. The y-component is

$$\mu_y^{\pi} = (-0{\cdot}035 - 0{\cdot}013/2 + 0{\cdot}038/2 - 0{\cdot}147 + 0{\cdot}038 - 0{\cdot}013/2)\; 1{\cdot}40 \times 4{\cdot}77$$

$$= -0{\cdot}157 \times 1{\cdot}40 \times 4{\cdot}77 \text{ D} = -1{\cdot}06 \text{ D}$$

The 4·77 is the electronic charge in appropriate units and the answer is expressed in Debyes. The moment is along the y-axis and towards the nitrogen atom having a magnitude of 1·06 D. Assuming a value of 1·0 D for the σ-bond moment, we obtain a value of 1·0 D as the total σ moment. This gives a total moment of 2·06 D. The experimental value for the dipole moment of pyridine is 2·22 D. We see that a reasonable agreement is obtained.

It is obvious from what has been said above that dipole moments are a very sensitive test of the wave function. Furthermore we have assumed that the centroids of the orbitals are coincident with the atoms. Although this is true for ordinary $2p$-orbitals it is not true of the orthogonalized $2p$-orbitals which we have used. These orbitals are neither well localized nor are they centrosymmetric. The consequences of this and a fuller discussion of the relation between ordinary and orthogonalized $2p_z$-orbitals will be given in the chapter on self-consistent field theory.

11. Free Valence

We have already noticed that a bond order is a measure of the delocalization of electrons from the adjacent atoms into the bond region. The bond order is a direct measure of the amount of charge located in the bond. If the effective number of electrons on an atom is a measure of its reactivity towards positively charged ions, then we can use the sum of the bond orders as an inverse measure of this. This is a wave-mechanical restatement of Thiele's theory of partial valence. Following Coulson (e.g. 1961) we can define a quantity called the bond number N_i which is the sum of the total bond orders of the bonds in which atom i is involved.

This concept may be illustrated with reference to butadiene (see p. 18). Each terminal carbon atom is engaged in the formation of three σ-bonds, two with hydrogen atoms and one with the neighbouring carbon atom. From Table 1 it is seen that the π-bond order between the two carbon atoms is 0·894. The quantity N_i is then equal to

$$3{\cdot}00+0{\cdot}894 = 3{\cdot}894 = N_1 = N_4$$

similarly for the internal atoms

$$N_2 = N_3 = 3{\cdot}00+0{\cdot}894+0{\cdot}447 = 4{\cdot}341$$

It is obvious from these values of N_i that the inner atoms are more deeply involved in bonding than the outer atoms. It is to be expected therefore that the terminal atoms will be more reactive than the inner atoms. This is indeed the case.

Coulson has shown that the maximum possible value for N_i (excluding triple bonds) is $4{\cdot}732 = N_{max}$. A quantity F_r may therefore be defined as

$$F_r = N_{max} - N_r \tag{29}$$

The quantity F_r is called the free valence of atom r. For butadiene it is seen that F_r has the values 0·838 and 0·391 for the outer and inner carbon atoms respectively. The free valence concept is then the wave-mechanical analogue of Thiele's partial valencies.

It is found that values of F_r greater than unity are usually associated with free radicals, values around 0·8 with terminal atoms in a chain. From Table 1 it can be seen that for benzene F_r has the value 0·40 for each carbon, which is an expression of the equivalence of the six carbon atoms in benzene with respect to reactivity. For internal atoms in an open conjugated chain, such as atoms 2 and 3 in butadiene, the values of F_r are less than 0·4. This reflects the reactive tendencies of the carbon atoms in these several environments.

The free valencies of atoms in a molecule are usually denoted by arrows diverging from the atoms with the values of F_r at the arrow heads. For butadiene we would show it in the following way

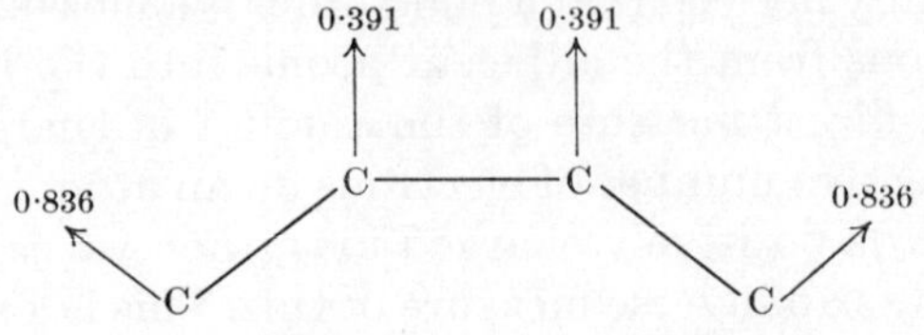

FIG. 9. Free valence for butadiene.

12. The Molecular Diagram

The numerical values obtained from the one-electron density function for conjugated and aromatic molecules may be conveniently summarized in the so-called molecular diagram (see, for example, Coulson, 1961). In Fig. 10 we show how the molecular diagram is constructed.

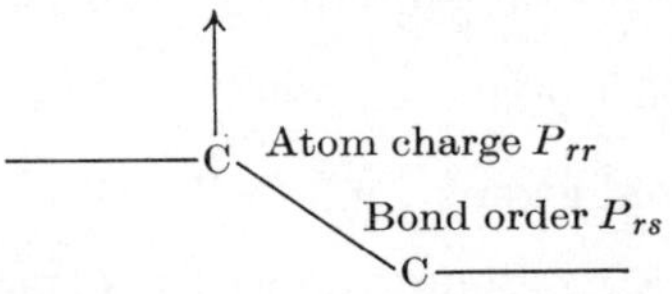

FIG. 10. The molecular diagram.

In Fig. 11 we give the molecular diagrams for some important molecules, butadiene, benzene, pyridine (with $\delta = 0{\cdot}50$), naphthalene.

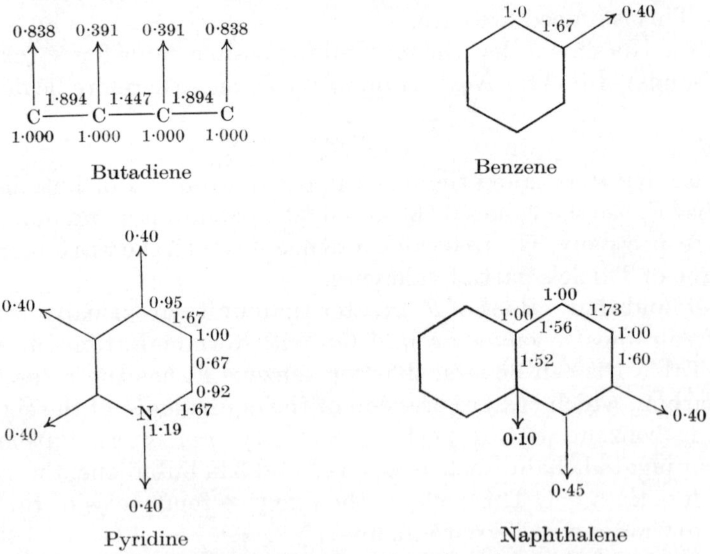

FIG. 11. Molecular diagrams for selected molecules.

The molecular diagrams can be used in the following ways.

1. The bond orders allow us to calculate bond lengths.
2. The bond orders show us the degree of localization of electrons in a "double" bond.
3. The charges on an atom allow us to say something about the reactivity of the various sites in the molecule.
4. The atom charges can be used to estimate dipole moments.
5. The values of the free valence enable us to say something about reactivity, particularly in alternant hydrocarbons where there are no net charges on the atoms and electrostatic forces can play no part.

13. Diamagnetic Susceptibility

It is found that there is a large diamagnetic anisotropy in aromatic molecules. The susceptibility measured in a direction perpendicular to the plane of the molecule is much larger than that in the plane of the molecule. This increase in the susceptibility arises from the presence of ring currents due to the π-electrons.

A method for calculating the susceptibility due to the π-electrons was given by London (1937). In the presence of an applied magnetic field the Hamiltonian for a single electron becomes

$$\mathscr{H} = -\frac{\hbar^2}{2m}\nabla^2+V-\frac{1}{2m}\left(\frac{i\hbar e}{c}\operatorname{div}\mathbf{A}+\frac{2i\hbar e}{c}A\operatorname{grad}+\frac{e^2}{c^2}|A|^2\right) \quad (30)$$

where A is the magnetic vector potential. If there is some symmetry operation which turns the molecule into itself, say $R(xyz)\to x',y',z$, then the Hamiltonian is invariant under this operation. The Hamiltonian is also invariant under the operations which leave the potential invariant, that is all operations which interchange like nuclei. In the presents of the field, however, such symmetry operations are restricted to those which correspond to rotations about the direction of the field, say about the z-axis. Wave functions which previously belonged to a degenerate eigenvalue will split under the influence of the field. With a uniform field and our choice of axes we have

$$\operatorname{div}A = 0 \quad |\mathbf{A}|^2 = \frac{H^2}{4}(x^2+y^2) = \frac{H^2}{4}(r^2-z^2)$$

$$A\operatorname{grad} = \frac{H}{2}\left(x\frac{\partial}{\partial y}-y\frac{\partial}{\partial x}\right) = \frac{H}{2}\frac{\partial}{\partial\phi} \quad (31)$$

London assumed that each molecular orbital could be represented by a linear combination of atomic orbitals modified to take into account the effects of the field. A suitable form for the orbital on atom r is

$$\phi_r(\overline{r-R_r}) = \phi_0(\overline{r-R_r})\exp(-2\pi i\alpha R_n A) \tag{32}$$

where ϕ_r and ϕ_0 are the atomic orbitals centred on atoms whose lattice vectors are R_r and the origin respectively. **A** is the vector potential and $\alpha = (e/hc)$.

Using this set of atomic orbitals, the energies of the molecular orbitals in the field are the roots of the secular determinant

$$|(E_0 - E)\,\delta_{rs} + \beta\epsilon_{rs}\,\eta_{rs}| = 0 \tag{33}$$

where δ_{rs} is the Kronecker delta and has the value unity if $r = s$ and zero otherwise. The other symbols are given by

$$E_0 = \int \phi_r^*(\overline{r-R_r})\,\mathscr{H}\,\phi_r(\overline{r-R_r}) \quad \text{(Coulomb integral)}$$

$$\beta_{rs} = \epsilon_{rs}\int \phi_r^*(\overline{r-R_r})\,\mathscr{H}\,\phi_s(r-R_s) \tag{34}$$

where

$$\epsilon_{rs} = \exp\{2\pi i\alpha(R_r - R_s).\bar{r}\times H\}$$

β_{rs} is the usual resonance integral modified by the exponential factors. There is an approximation made in withdrawing the exponential factor outside of the integral for the resonance integral, $\bar{r}$ is then given the mean value of r_r and r_s appropriate to the bond r—s. The Coulomb integrals are again assumed to be the same value for each atom and, as usual in this approximation, we neglect resonance integrals between atoms more than one bond-length apart. This is equivalent to writing $\eta_{rs} = 1$ for nearest neighbours and equal to zero otherwise.

Although the secular determinant is only slightly modified by the presence of these ϵ factors, it is now extremely difficult to solve, and solution is only practicable in the simplest cases or where some considerable factorization is possible due to symmetry or other causes.

The problem can be considerably simplified by using a geometrical interpretation of ϵ_{rs} suggested by London. When the magnetic field is uniform and perpendicular to the plane of the molecule, the exponent has the form $2\pi i\alpha HS_{rs}$ where S_{rs} is the area contained by the triangle with vertices at atoms r, s and the origin. It must also be counted algebraically so that $S_{rs} = -S_{rs}$. Since a bond p—q can be brought into coincidence with r—s by a simple translation, there is a simple relationship between ϵ_{rs} and ϵ_{pq}.

$$\epsilon_{pq} = \epsilon_{rs}\times\exp\{-2\pi i\alpha H\times(\text{area swept out in translation of } r\text{—}s)\} \tag{35}$$

Choosing, say, atom 1 in the ring as origin and defining a quantity

$k = \exp\{-2\pi i\alpha HS\}$, where S is the area of one ring, the secular determinant now has a simple form which can be solved by standard methods.

In the expansion of the secular determinant we obtain a polynomial in E which can be solved for the eigenvalues of E in the usual manner. The expression for the energy of a system in a magnetic field is given by

$$E = E_0 - \tfrac{1}{2}\chi H^2 \tag{36}$$

where E_0 is the energy in the absence of the field, χ the diamagnetic susceptibility and the term in H^2 describes the effect of the applied field. If there was a paramagnetic contribution then this would be shown by the presence of a linear term in H which is omitted in (36) which assumes a diamagnetic contribution only. Therefore in our expansion of the secular determinant, if we rearrange the expressions for the orbital energies as a power series in H, then the coefficient of H^2 will give the diamagnetic susceptibility of the π-electrons, hence the diamagnetic anisotropy $\Delta\chi$. In general there will be no term in H. McWeeny (1951) has shown that terms in H can occur, but they are degenerate and give no observable contribution to the energy. Summation over all of the occupied orbitals gives the total diamagnetic susceptibility.

McWeeny (1951) has shown as a result of London-type calculations that the diamagnetic anisotropy for the polyphenyl series may be expressed by the simple relation

$$\Delta\chi/\Delta\chi_{\text{benz}} = 0{\cdot}859n + 0{\cdot}153 \quad (n \geqslant 2) \tag{37}$$

where $\Delta\chi_{\text{benz}}$ is the anisotropy for benzene, and n the number of rings in the system concerned. Inclusion of overlap gives a similar equation

$$\Delta\chi/\Delta\chi_{\text{benz}} = 0{\cdot}805n + 0{\cdot}148 \tag{38}$$

McWeeny (1952) has found that the anisotropy of the polyacenes may be expressed by the series

$$\frac{\Delta\chi}{\Delta\chi_{\text{benz}}} = -0{\cdot}47 + 1{\cdot}31n + 0{\cdot}007n^2 \quad (n \geqslant 4) \tag{39}$$

In a series of papers McWeeny (1951a,b, 1952, 1953) has calculated the diamagnetic susceptibilities of the polyphenyl series, the polyacene series, and those many-ring fused molecules which have a high degree of symmetry. In the last paper in the series he summarizes his results on forty molecules and draws the following conclusions:

"(i) Addition of a CH_2 group to a ring leads to a reduction in the anisotropy. The addition of a number of groups may be almost equivalent in effect to removing the ring from the molecule.

(ii) Addition of either of the groups —C≡H or —CH=CH_2 has little effect on $\Delta\chi$.

(iii) Addition of complete rings, joined to the original system by single links gives an increase in $\Delta\chi$ slightly less than would be expected in the absence of any conjugation across the bonds.

(iv) Addition of complete rings by condensation leads invariably to an increase in $\Delta\chi$ which (in units of $\Delta\chi_{\text{benz}}$) is never appreciably less than unity per added ring and is often much greater. The magnitude of the increment is dependent on the geometry of the whole molecule and the site of the addition."

14. Force Constants

The potential energy of a set of vibrating particles is dependent solely on the configuration of the particles. We shall be concerned here with a vibrating molecule in which the nuclei are the vibrating particles. Let $q_1, q_2 \ldots$ be a set of co-ordinates which describe the internuclear distances and bond angles in the molecule, then the potential energy V may be expanded as a Taylor series about the equilibrium configuration $\bar{q}_1, \bar{q}_2 \ldots$,

$$V(q_1, q_2 \ldots) = V(\bar{q}_1, \bar{q}_2 \ldots) + \sum_i \frac{\partial V}{\partial \bar{q}_i}(q - \bar{q}_i) + \frac{1}{2}\sum_{ij} \frac{\partial^2 V}{\partial \bar{q}_i \, \partial \bar{q}_j}(q_i - \bar{q}_i)(q_j - \bar{q}_j)$$

$$+ \text{higher order terms} \tag{40}$$

Since the $\bar{q}_i$ define the equilibrium configuration then the first sum vanishes, and if the displacements $(q_i - \bar{q}_i)$ are small the terms of the third order and higher will be negligible. We can therefore write

$$V(q) - V(\bar{q}) = \frac{1}{2}\sum_{ij} \frac{\partial^2 V}{\partial \bar{q}_i \, \partial \bar{q}_j}(q_i - \bar{q}_i)(q_j - \bar{q}_j) \tag{41}$$

A physically realistic way of choosing the set of co-ordinates is to assign a co-ordinate to each bond and to each bond angle in the molecule. The potential energy expressed in such a way is known as the valence force potential energy. Under such circumstances the second-order derivatives occurring in (41) are known as force constants or interaction constants, depending upon their form. We define

(i) $\dfrac{\partial^2 V}{\partial \bar{q}^2}$ as the force constant of the ith bond, and

(ii) $\dfrac{\partial^2 V}{\partial q_i \, \partial q_j}$ as the interaction constant of the bonds i and j.

In many cases it so happens that the interaction constants are either small or zero. This is not, however, a general rule and such terms must always be looked for.

Coulson and Longuet-Higgins have discussed the evaluation of force constants in aromatic molecules using the Hückel theory, and in what follows we shall follow their argument very closely.

For any change in the configuration of an unsaturated hydrocarbon the change in potential energy may be written as

$$\delta V = \delta E + \delta \epsilon \tag{42}$$

where E is the energy of the σ-bonds and ϵ the energy of the π-electrons. The change in σ-bond energy may be written (Lennard-Jones, 1937) as

$$E = \sum_r \tfrac{1}{2}\sigma(x_r - s)^2 \tag{43}$$

where σ, s are the force constant and length of a pure σ-bond, and x_r is the length of the bond r. The π-electron energy is easily expressed in terms of the resonance integrals β. We therefore need to know how the resonance integral varies with bond length. We shall take this matter up in detail in Chapter 5. Coulson and Longuet-Higgins in their work used a dependence suggested by Lennard-Jones, namely

$$2\beta_r = \text{const} + \tfrac{1}{2}\kappa(x_r - d)^2 - \tfrac{1}{2}\sigma(x_r - s)^2 \tag{44}$$

from which we obtain

$$\frac{d\beta}{dx_r} = \tfrac{1}{2}\kappa(x_r - d) - \tfrac{1}{2}\sigma(x_r - s) \tag{45}$$

where κ, d are the force constant and length of a pure double bond.

Using (42) the force constant for a bond r may be broken down into a σ and a π part,

$$\frac{\partial^2 V}{\partial \bar{x}_r^2} = \frac{\partial^2 E}{\partial \bar{x}_r^2} + \frac{\partial^2 \epsilon}{\partial \bar{x}_r^2} \tag{46}$$

Now ϵ is a simple function of the resonance integrals β, and each β is a function of the bond length, the right-hand side of (46) becomes

$$\frac{\partial^2 E}{\partial \bar{x}_r^2} + \frac{d^2\beta}{d\bar{x}_r^2}\frac{\partial \epsilon}{\partial \beta_r} + \left(\frac{d\beta_r}{d\bar{x}_r}\right)^2 \frac{\partial^2 \epsilon}{\partial \beta_r^2}$$

$$= \sigma + (\kappa - \sigma)P_r + \{\tfrac{1}{2}\kappa(\bar{x}_r - d) - \tfrac{1}{2}\sigma(\bar{x}_r - s)\}^2\, 2\pi_{r,r} \tag{47}$$

where the $\pi_{r,r}$ is the self-bond polarizability of the rth bond introduced by Coulson & Longuet-Higgins (1947). (These quantities will be discussed further in Chapter 5.) We have also made use of the relation $\partial\epsilon/\partial\beta_r = 2P_r$ (P_r the π-bond order of the rth bond) (Coulson & Longuet-Higgins, 1947). From (43) and (45) is follows that the equilibrium bond length $\bar{x}_r$ is given by

$$\bar{x}_r = \frac{d\kappa P_r + s\sigma(1 - P_r)}{\kappa P_r + \sigma(1 - P_r)} \tag{48}$$

Substitution of (48) in (47) then gives

$$\frac{\partial^2 V}{\partial \bar{x}_r^2} = \sigma(1-P)_r + \kappa P_r + \frac{1}{2}\left\{\frac{\kappa\sigma(s-d)}{\sigma(1-P_r)+\kappa P_r}\right\}^2 \pi_{r,r} \quad (49)$$

The interaction constant of bonds r and s is given by

$$\begin{aligned}\frac{\partial^2 V}{\partial \bar{x}_r\,\partial \bar{x}_s} &= \frac{\partial^2 E}{\partial \bar{x}_r\,\partial \bar{x}_s} + \frac{\partial^2 \epsilon}{\partial \bar{x}_r\,\partial \bar{x}_s} \\ &= \frac{d\beta_r\,d\beta_s}{d\bar{x}_r\,d\bar{x}_s}\frac{\partial^2 \epsilon}{\partial \beta_r\,\partial \beta_s} \\ &= \frac{1}{2}\left\{\frac{\kappa\sigma(s-d)}{\sigma(1-P_r)+\kappa P_r}\right\}\left\{\frac{\kappa\sigma(s-d)}{\sigma(1-P_r)+\kappa P_s}\right\}\pi_{r,s} \quad (50)\end{aligned}$$

where $\pi_{r,s}$ is the mutual bond polarizability of bonds r and s.

It is seen that the force constant for a bond may be expressed as the sum of two terms, one which is linear in the bond order and the second which depends on the self-polarizability.

This theory was applied by Coulson and Longuet-Higgins to benzene, naphthalene and butadiene. Their results are in fairly good agreement with the experimental values.

15. Electronic Spectra

An excited state can be approximately described by promoting electrons from occupied to unoccupied orbitals of the ground state problem. The energy required to do this (the excitation energy) is given in the simple MO picture which we are discussing here by

$$E_{J\to K} = E_K - E_J = \alpha + x_K\beta - (\alpha + x_J\beta) = (x_K - x_J)\beta \quad (51)$$

These calculated transition energies may be correlated with the observed electronic spectrum of the molecule. In Table 6 we give the lowest observed transition energy, together with the difference in orbital energy, between the first vacant and top filled orbital in the ground state for a few polyenes.

TABLE 6. Spectra of selected molecules

	Energy (ν)	Orbital energy difference (β)	Ratio
Ethylene	61,500	2·000	30,750
Butadiene	46,080	1·236	37,250
Hexatriene	39,750	0·890	44,500

Division of the observed energy by the difference in orbital energy gives another method to determine β. In the third column of Table 6 this is done and it can be seen that the values of β are not consistent even for the three molecules considered, and in fact β increases as the chain length increases. The average value of 37,500$\bar{\nu}$ corresponds to a β value of about 4·7 eV or 108 kcal/mole. This value is unrelated to any of the values obtained by any other method.

In Table 7 we give corresponding values for the lowest band in the polyacenes.

TABLE 7. Spectra of polyacenes

	Energy	E	Ratio
Benzene	37,900	2·000	19,000
Naphthalene	31,800	1·236	25,500
Anthracene	26,400	0·828	31,000
Tetracene	21,200	0·590	36,000
Pentacene	17,400	0·439	39,500

Again we see that there is no correlation at all between the values of β obtained from the molecules in the series. We see again that as we increase the number of rings in the system the value of β tends to increase.

With an averaged value of β we can predict the position of the first band to within about half of an electron volt at best. When we look at the higher transitions, however, there is no correlation whatsoever and this method fails completely.

The reason for the failure is probably clear when we look at these results, bearing in mind the properties of alternant hydrocarbons. In Section 3 it was stated that the orbital energies lie symmetrically about the energy zero α and that these orbitals are also related through their coefficients. Let us label the molecular orbitals A, B, C... in descending energy order from the energy zero for the bonding orbitals and A', B', ... etc. in ascending energy order for the unoccupied orbitals. We then have the simple relation that $E_{A'} = -E_A$, and the coefficients of the orbitals in A and A' are also simply related. In cases of degeneracies we always label the orbitals with related coefficients with the same letter. Using this notation, consider the top two filled orbitals and the lowest two empty orbitals in a general alternant. In our notation these will be B, A, A' and B' in ascending energy order. Then owing to the alternant character $E_{B'} = -E_B$ and $E_{A'} = -E_A$ and the transition energies of the transitions $A \rightarrow B'$ and $B \rightarrow A'$ will be equal, viz.

$$E_{B'} - E_A = E_{A'} - E_B \tag{52}$$

It is clear therefore that the one-determinant wave functions of the two excited states are degenerate and will interact heavily, since they have the same symmetry. The best mixtures will be found by solution of the secular problem

$$\begin{vmatrix} H_{A-B', B\to A'} - E & H_{A\to B', B\to A'} \\ H_{B\to A', A\to B'} & H_{B\to A', B\to A'} - E \end{vmatrix} = 0 \tag{53}$$

solution of which will split the degenerate states into two new states. This was first discussed in the case of general alternants by Dewar & Longuet-Higgins (1954) although it was considered for the benzene molecule by Goeppert-Mayer & Sklar (1938).

Unfortunately, however, even this elaboration does not give a satisfactory interpretation of the observed ultra-violet absorption spectra. A satisfactory interpretation can be achieved only by using a self-consistent field Hamiltonian in which the interactions between the π-electrons are properly included, followed by even more extensive configuration than that which occurs in the way discussed above.

The degeneracy discussed above disappears when we go to a heterocyclic molecule derived from an alternant hydrocarbon by substitution. Here the degeneracy in the transition energy disappears because the orbitals are no longer symmetric about α. The need for configuration interaction, however, remains.

Calculation of spectral transitions affords a further method for the determination of δ. The change of the Coulomb integral will have an effect on the orbital energies of the heterocyclic derivative. We can therefore vary δ until we obtain a fit with the experimental data for a series of related molecules. Davies (1955) did this for the series pyridine, pyridazine, pyrimidine, pyrazine and sym-triazine. He used the value of δ which gave the correct value for pyridine and then used this value to calculate the others. His results are shown in Table 8. Davies used the

TABLE 8. Spectra of azines

	Predicted	Expt. (eV)
Pyridine	4·95	4·95
Pyridazine	4·98	5·00
Pyrimidine	4·98	5·15
Pyrazine	4·54	4·77
sym-Triazine	5·52	5·62

value 0·58 for δ. It can be seen that a reasonable agreement is found for the series. However, when we go to the higher transitions there is no agreement with experiment.

16. Summary

In this chapter we have discussed the simple model in which the electrons are assumed to move in one-electron orbitals in an "averaged" field. In particular, the interactions of the π-electrons have been ignored. This is one of the serious deficiencies of the model.

The model has then been used to look at the properties of the molecule which are dependent on either the π-electron distribution or upon the orbital energies of the π-electrons.

It has been noted in particular that we are unable to suggest any value for the two empirical parameters α and β. Indeed a different value appears to be necessary for each property considered and, in the case of spectra, even for each molecule considered. One of the difficulties which arises here, and which partly explains why we do not obtain reproducible results, is that the variation of β with bond length has not been considered. This point will be taken up later in Chapter 5.

It has been seen that the change in the Coulomb integral due to a heterocyclic atom may be determined in several ways. However, although a certain measure of success is obtained with values around 0·5 for nitrogen, we are still unable to obtain a value which may be used to discuss several properties. One of the reasons for this failure is that the dependence of α on the π-electron density on a given atom has not been taken into consideration. This is a further point which will be properly taken into account within the context of self-consistent field theory.

Qualitatively, however, we have seen that the Hückel model gives us a good understanding of the properties of conjugated and aromatic molecules. It will be seen later that the general picture which is given by the Hückel model may be taken over into self-consistent theory.

References

Chirgwin, B. H. & Coulson, C. A. (1950). *Proc. R. Soc.* **A201**, 196.
Coulson, C. A. (1939). *Proc. R. Soc.* **A169**, 413.
Coulson, C. A. (1951). *Proc. R. Soc.* **A207**, 91.
Coulson, C. A. (1961). "Valence", 2nd edition. Oxford University Press, London.
Coulson, C. A. & Rushbrooke, G. S. (1940). *Proc. Camb. phil. Soc.* **36**, 193.
Coulson, C. A. & Longuet-Higgins, H. C. (1947). *Proc. R. Soc.* **A191**, 39; **A192**, 16.
Coulson, C. A. & Longuet-Higgins, H. C. (1948). *Proc. R. Soc.* **A193**, 447; **A195**, 188.
Coulson, C. A. & Altmann, S. A. (1952). *Trans. Faraday Soc.* **48**, 293.
Davies, D. W. (1955). *Trans. Faraday Soc.* **51**, 449.
Dewar, M. J. S. & Longuet-Higgins, H. C. (1954). *Proc. phys. Soc.* **A67**, 795.
Glockler, G. (1953). *J. chem. Phys.* **21**, 1247.
Goeppert-Mayer, M. & Sklar, A. L. (1938). *J. chem. Phys.* **6**, 645.
Hückel, E. P. (1931). *Z. Phys.* **70**, 204; **72**, 310.
Koopmans, T. (1933). *Physica, 's Grav.* **1**, 104.

Lennard-Jones, J. E. (1937). *Proc. R. Soc.* **A158**, 280.
London, F. (1937). *J. Phys. Radium* **8**, 397.
McWeeny, R. (1951). *Proc. phys. Soc.* **64**, 261, 921.
McWeeny, R. (1952). *Proc. phys. Soc.* **65**, 839.
McWeeny, R. (1953). *Proc. phys. Soc.* **66**, 714.
McWeeny, R. (1956a). *Proc. R. Soc.* **A233**, 496.
McWeeny, R. (1956b). *Proc. R. Soc.* **A237**, 355.
McWeeny, R. (1959). *Phys. Rev.* **114**, 1528.
McWeeny, R. & Peacock, T. E. (1957). *Proc. phys. Soc.* **A70**, 41.
Mulliken, R. S. & Parr, R. G. (1951). *J. chem. Phys.* **19**, 1271.
Perez, S. S., Herraez, M. A., Igea, F. J. & Esteve, J. (1955). *An. R. Soc. esp. Fís. Quím.* **51B**, 91.
Pritchard, H. O. & Sumner, F. H. (1955). *Trans. Faraday Soc.* **51**, 457.
Wheland, G. W. & Pauling, L. (1935). *J. Am. chem. Soc.* **57**, 2086.

CHAPTER 3

The Valence Bond Theory

1. Introduction

In the molecular orbital theory of the hydrogen molecule we feed the two electrons into the lowest molecular orbital. This orbital has the form

$$\psi = N(\phi_a + \phi_b) \tag{1}$$

The molecular wave function then has the form

$$\Psi = \psi(1)\,\alpha(1)\,\psi(2)\,\beta(2) - \psi(1)\,\beta(1)\,\psi(2)\,\beta(2) \tag{2}$$

Substituting for ψ from (1) into (2) we get

$$\Psi = N^2(\phi_a(1)\,\phi_a(2) + \phi_a(1)\,\phi_b(2) + \phi_b(1)\,\phi_a(2) + \phi_b(2)\,\phi_b(2))$$
$$\times\,(\alpha(1)\,\beta(2) - \beta(1)\,\alpha(2)) \tag{3}$$

Examining the individual terms in this expansion it is seen that the first and last terms correspond to both electrons being localized on atoms a and b respectively. In other words these terms correspond to ionic states H^-H^+ and H^+H^- respectively. The other two terms correspond to the covalent states in which the electrons are shared equally between the two atoms. The molecular orbital theory then gives equal weight to ionic and covalent structures. Since the electron affinity for hydrogen is much lower than its ionization potential, these structures cannot have the same stability as the covalent structures.

Heitler and London suggested that a more reasonable wave function for the hydrogen molecule is

$$\Psi = N(\phi_a(1)\,\phi_b(2) + \phi_b(1)\,\phi_a(2))\,(\alpha(1)\,\beta(2) - \beta(1)\,\alpha(2)) \tag{4}$$

where only the covalent structures are included. Later developments of the theory included ionic terms but with a much smaller weight than the covalent ones. One of the most important features of this theory is that it formulates in quantum-mechanical terms the theory of the covalent bond which was then popular among chemists. This theory demanded the perfect pairing and sharing of the two electrons which made up the bond. The Heitler–London theory simply gave this picture a mathematical formulation. The problem in valence bond theory is to construct spin eigenfunctions which correspond to this perfect pairing and are at the same time eigenfunctions of S^2. We shall go further into this question in Section 3.

2. Extension to Aromatic Molecules

Kekulé had suggested that in order to account for the chemical properties of benzene, it must be assumed that the two possible assignments for the three double bonds (see Fig. 12) must both be included somehow.

FIG. 12. Kekulé structures for benzene

Proceeding to a quantum-mechanical formulation we can write a wave function for the two double bonds in the following way

$$\Psi_1 = \phi_1(1)\,\alpha(1)\,\phi_2(2)\,\beta(2)\,\phi_3(3)\,\beta(3)\,\phi_4(4)\,\alpha(4)\,\phi_5(5)\,\alpha(5)\,\phi_6(6)\,\beta(6) \quad (4a)$$

which corresponds to a double bond between atoms 1 and 2, 3 and 4, and 5 and 6. Alternatively we may write the wave function as

$$\Psi_2 = \phi_1(1)\,\alpha(1)\,\phi_2(2)\,\alpha(2)\,\phi_3(3)\,\beta(3)\,\phi_4(4)\,\beta(4)\,\phi_5(5)\,\alpha(5)\,\phi_6(6)\,\beta(6) \quad (4b)$$

which corresponds to an assignment of the double bonds between atoms 2 and 3, 4 and 5, and 6 and 1. The true wave function is in fact neither of these possibilities but to a first approximation is a linear combination of them both

$$\Psi = \frac{1}{\sqrt{2}}(\Psi_1 + c\Psi_2) \quad (5)$$

where c is a constant of modulus unity.

This form of wave function in which the functions corresponding to different assignments of the bonds are mixed is known as a resonance hybrid. The theory which leads to it is known as the Valence Bond Theory or Resonance Theory. The structures which are included in the formulation of the theory are frequently known as Canonical Structures. It should be emphasized that these canonical structures have no objective reality.

The wave function can be included by the inclusion of further structures. In the description of the benzene molecule it is usual to mix in the three structures which are known as the Dewar Structures. These are shown in Fig. 13.

The weight with which these structures are included in the wave function is determined by a variational calculation and we shall discuss the evaluation of matrix elements of the Hamiltonian between structures in a later section.

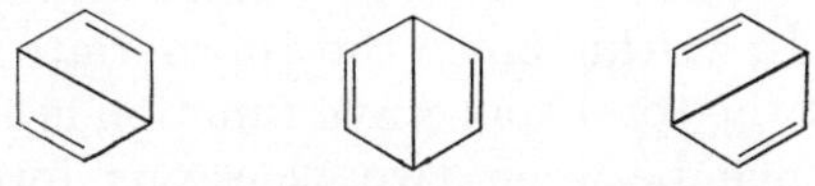

FIG. 13. Dewar structures for benzene.

For any aromatic or conjugated hydrocarbon we can write down the possible set of structures which correspond to perfect pairing of the electrons which make up the double bonds and then evaluate the weights with which they occur in the wave function in the usual way. To obtain a better wave function we should include ionic structures as well. It is obvious that for any but the simplest cases this problem becomes one of great mathematical complexity.

3. Spin Eigenfunctions

From what has been said above it is obvious that a general formulation of valence bond requires a way of setting up spin eigenfunctions with the correct "pairing" properties to describe the structure under consideration. In a molecule the operators M^2 and M_z no longer commute with the Hamiltonian owing to the lack of spherical symmetry. However, S^2 and S_z still commute with the Hamiltonian and we can construct spin eigenfunctions which are simultaneously eigenfunctions of S^2 and S_z which are associated with the eigenfunctions of the Hamiltonian. When this is done the secular determinant factorizes in the way discussed in Chapter 1.

The spin function is immediately an eigenfunction of S_z and has the eigenvalue

$$s_z = \tfrac{1}{2}(n_\alpha - n_\beta)\hbar \tag{5}$$

where n_α is the number of α spins and n_β is the number of electrons with β spin in the function.

If we have four electrons then there are twenty-four possible eigenfunctions for S_z. Classifying these according to their values of S_z we have

Eigenvalue (in units of $\hbar$)	-2	-1	0	1	2
No. of eigenfunctions	1	4	6	4	1

From the six which have spin eigenvalues of zero we can construct valence bond structures which correspond to perfect pairing.

This problem of four electrons is in fact the problem of the structure of the cyclobutadiene molecule. The problem then is how to assign the two double bonds to the molecule. There can either be bonds between a and b, and between c and d; or else between b and c and a and d; or between a and c and b and d. In writing down the appropriate spin wave function we must ensure that the total spin wave function is antisymmetric with respect to interchange between two electrons forming a bond and symmetric with respect to interchange between two electrons not engaged in the same bond.

The six spin functions which have eigenvalues of S_z equal to zero are

	a	b	c	d
η_1	α	α	β	β
η_2	α	β	α	β
η_3	β	α	α	β
η_4	α	β	β	α
η_5	β	α	β	α
η_6	β	β	α	α

The spin eigenfunction which represents bonds between a and b, and c and d is given by

$$\eta_{ab,cd} = \tfrac{1}{2}(\eta_2-\eta_3-\eta_4+\eta_5) \quad (6)$$

$\eta_{ab,cd}$ must be antisymmetric with respect to interchange of electrons assigned to AOs which form a bond, i.e. a and b or c and d, whilst interchange of electrons between orbitals not engaged in bonding (e.g. a and c or d, or b and c or d) should be symmetric. That for bonds between b and c and a and d is given by

$$\eta_{bc,ad} = \tfrac{1}{2}(\eta_1-\eta_2-\eta_5+\eta_6) \quad (7)$$

and for bonds between a and c, and b and d we have the function

$$\eta_{ac,bd} = \tfrac{1}{2}(\eta_1-\eta_3-\eta_4+\eta_6) \quad (8)$$

but it is obvious that the third equation is simply the sum of the other two.

$$\eta_{ac,bd} = \eta_{ab,cd}+\eta_{bc,ad} \quad (9)$$

This leads to a general rule which we shall discuss later, that any bond eigenfunction which involves crossing of bonds in a molecule may be written as a linear combination of eigenfunction which involve bonds which do not cross.

We must now see whether these bond eigenfunctions are also eigenfunctions of S^2. To do this we make use of the relations (see Chapter 1, Section 4)

$$\left.\begin{aligned}(S_{x1}+iS_{y1})\,\alpha(1) &= 0\\ (S_{x1}+iS_{y1})\,\beta(1) &= \hbar\alpha(1)\\ (S_{x1}-iS_{y1})\,\alpha(1) &= \hbar\beta(1)\\ (S_{x1}-iS_{y1})\,\beta(1) &= 0\end{aligned}\right\}\begin{aligned}&\text{and}\\ &(S_x+iS_y) = \sum_n (S_{xn}+iS_{yn})\\ &(S_x-iS_y) = \sum_n (S_{xn}-iS_{yn})\end{aligned}\quad (10)$$

and

$$S^2 = (S_x-iS_y)(S_x+iS_y)+\hbar S_z+S_z^2 \quad (11)$$

It is found that (6) and (7) are indeed eigenfunctions of the operator S^2 with eigenvalue zero. They are in fact the only functions with this eigenvalue in the problem which we are discussing. The bond eigenfunctions which can be written corresponding to one bond have eigenvalues of $3\hbar^2$ and the function which corresponds to no bonds has the eigenvalue $6\hbar^2$. Since the number of functions with eigenvalue of S^2 of zero is two, the solution of the problem describing the mixing of the valence structures will be merely the solution of a determinant of the second order. The wave functions for these structures may be written as

$$\begin{aligned}\Psi_{ab,cd} = \frac{1}{2}\Big\{&\frac{1}{4!^{1/2}}|\phi_a(1)\,\alpha(1)\,\phi_b(2)\,\beta(2)\,\phi_c(3)\,\alpha(3)\,\phi_d(4)\,\beta(4)|\\ &-\frac{1}{4!^{1/2}}|\phi_a(1)\,\beta(1)\,\phi_b(2)\,\alpha(2)\,\phi_c(3)\,\alpha(3)\,\beta\phi_d(4)\,(4)|\\ &-\frac{1}{4!^{1/2}}|\phi_a(1)\,\alpha(1)\,\phi_b(2)\,\beta(2)\,\phi_c(3)\,\beta(3)\,\phi_d(4)\,\alpha(4)|\\ &+\frac{1}{4!^{1/2}}|\phi_a(1)\,\beta(1)\,\phi_b(2)\,\alpha(2)\,\phi_c(3)\,\beta(3)\,\phi_d(4)\,\alpha(4)|\Big\}\end{aligned} \quad (12)$$

corresponding to (6) and

$$\begin{aligned}\Psi_{bc,ad} = \frac{1}{2}\Big\{&\frac{1}{4!^{1/2}}|\phi_a(1)\,\alpha(1)\,\phi_b(2)\,\alpha(2)\,\phi_c(3)\,\beta(3)\,\phi_d(4)\,\beta(4)|\\ &-\frac{1}{4!^{1/2}}|\phi_a(1)\,\alpha(1)\,\phi_b(2)\,\beta(2)\,\phi_c(3)\,\alpha(3)\,\phi_d(4)\,\beta(4)|\\ &-\frac{1}{4!^{1/2}}|\phi_a(1)\,\beta(1)\,\phi_b(2)\,\alpha(2)\,\phi_c(3)\,\beta(3)\,\phi_d(4)\,\alpha(4)|\\ &+\frac{1}{4!^{1/2}}|\phi_a(1)\,\beta(1)\,\phi_b(2)\,\beta(2)\,\phi_c(3)\,\alpha(3)\,\phi_d(4)\,\alpha(4)|\Big\}\end{aligned} \quad (13)$$

corresponding to (7), where the ϕ_i are the $2p_z$ atomic orbitals on atoms a, b, c and d respectively.

It remains now to evaluate the matrix elements of the Hamiltonian between the functions (12) and (13).

4. Evaluation of Hamiltonian Elements

We must now evaluate elements of the Hamiltonian and of the overlap matrix between the determinantal functions which make up the wave functions (12) and (13). Let us write

$$\psi_1 = \frac{1}{\sqrt{4!}}|\phi_a(1)\,\alpha(1)\,\phi_b(2)\,\alpha(2)\,\phi_c(3)\,\beta(3)\,\phi_d(4)\,\beta(4)| \tag{14}$$

which is the determinant derived from the four space orbitals and the spin function η_1.

Similarly let us write

$$\psi_2 = \frac{1}{\sqrt{4!}}|\phi_a(1)\,\alpha(1)\,\phi_b(2)\,\beta(2)\,\phi_c(3)\,\alpha(3)\,\phi_d(4)\,\beta(4)| \tag{15}$$

where the spin part is described using η_2.

The element of the Hamiltonian H_{12} between these two functions may now be evaluated. Because of the orthogonality of the spin functions all of the terms vanish except for those where the spins match identically. Integrating over the spins we have

$$\begin{aligned} H_{12} &= \int \psi_1 H \psi_2\, dv \\ &= -(\phi_a\phi_b\phi_c\phi_d|H|\phi_a\phi_c\phi_b\phi_d) + (\phi_a\phi_b\phi_c\phi_d|H|\phi_a\phi_c\phi_d\phi_b) \\ &\quad + (\phi_a\phi_b\phi_c\phi_d|H|\phi_c\phi_a\phi_b\phi_d) - (\phi_a\phi_b\phi_c\phi_d|H|\phi_c\phi_a\phi_d\phi_b) \end{aligned} \tag{16}$$

where

$$\begin{aligned} &(\phi_a\phi_b\phi_c\phi_d|H|\phi_a\phi_c\phi_b\phi_d) \\ &\qquad = \int \phi_a(1)\,\phi_b(2)\,\phi_c(3)\,\phi_d(4)\,H\phi_a(1)\,\phi_c(2)\,\phi_b(3)\,\phi_d(4)\,dv \end{aligned}$$

If we assume that the functions form an orthogonal set, then all integrals involving the interchange of more than one or two electrons will vanish. All of the integrals in (16) will vanish except the first, let us call this integral (bc), then

$$H_{12} = -(bc) \tag{17}$$

It is obvious that as a general rule we can say that the matrix element of the Hamiltonian between two ψ-functions is zero except when the functions differ only in the assignment of two electrons. It then has the value of minus the corresponding exchange integral.

The diagonal elements are evaluated in the same way. For the integral H_{11} we have

$$H_{11} = (\phi_a \phi_b \phi_c \phi_d|H|\phi_a \phi_b \phi_c \phi_d) - (\phi_a \phi_b \phi_c \phi_d|H|\phi_a \phi_b \phi_d \phi_c) - (\phi_a \phi_b \phi_c \phi_d|H|\phi_b \phi_a \phi_c \phi_d) \quad (18)$$

Making the same assumptions about the non-vanishing of the individual terms we have

$$H_{11} = Q - (cd) - (ab) \quad (19)$$

As a general rule we can say that the diagonal element of the Hamiltonian H_{ii} has the value Q (the "Coulomb" integral) minus the sum of all exchange integrals between orbitals having the same spin.

In this way all of the integrals occurring in the matrix elements of the Hamiltonian between the functions (12) and (13) can be evaluated in the straightforward fashion. The elements are found to have the values:

$$\left.\begin{aligned}(\psi_{ab,cd}|H|\psi_{ab,cd}) &= Q - \tfrac{1}{2}\{(ac)+(ad)+(bc)+(bd)\}+(ab)+(cd)\\(\psi_{bc,da}|H|\psi_{bc,da}) &= Q - \tfrac{1}{2}\{(ab)+(ac)+(cd)+(bd)\}+(ad)+(bc)\\(\psi_{ab,cd}|H|\psi_{bc,da}) &= -\tfrac{1}{2}Q+(ac)+(bd)-\tfrac{1}{2}\{(ab)+(ad)+(bc)+(cd)\}\end{aligned}\right\} \quad (20)$$

and $S_{ab,cd;ab,cd} = S_{bc,da;bc,da} = 1$ and $S_{ab,cd,bc,da} = -\frac{1}{2}$.

It only remains now to evaluate the Q and the exchange integrals over atomic orbitals. The evaluation of these integrals raises problems, some of which will be discussed in Chapter 5.

In discussing the structure of aromatic hydrocarbons we can make some assumptions which are parallel to those made in the Hückel theory using molecular orbitals. The Coulomb integral Q may be regarded as being independent of the environment of the atom in the molecule. Further, it may be regarded as an empirical parameter. With regard to the exchange integrals we may, to a first approximation, disregard all but those involving nearest neighbours. Let us call this integral α. Again we assume it to be independent of its environment and determine its value by appeal to experiment.

We can now complete the butadiene problem. Let us denote $\psi_{ab,cd}$ by ψ_A and $\psi_{bc,da}$ by ψ_B. Making the approximations discussed above, equations (20) become

$$\left.\begin{aligned}H_{AA} &= Q+\alpha\\H_{BB} &= Q+\alpha\end{aligned}\quad H_{AB} = -\tfrac{1}{2}Q-2\alpha\right\} \quad (21)$$

The wave function is then determined by solution of the secular determinant

$$\begin{vmatrix}H_{AA}-E & H_{AB}-ES_{AB}\\H_{BB}-ES_{BA} & H_{BB}-E\end{vmatrix} = 0 \quad (22)$$

The roots of the determinant have the values $Q \pm 2\alpha$. Since α is a negative quantity the state with energy $Q+2\alpha$ corresponds to the ground state. The energy of the two individual states which interact is $Q+\alpha$, hence the state formed by mixing the two structures is more stable by an amount α than either of the individual structures. This gain in energy is known as the resonance energy and we shall discuss it further in the next section.

To complete the cyclobutadiene calculation we have only to calculate the resultant wave function associated with the ground state. Substitution of the value $Q+2\alpha$ for E in (22) leads to the normalized wave function

$$\Psi = \frac{1}{(2-2s)^{1/2}}(\psi_A - \psi_B) \tag{23}$$

In carrying out a calculation using the valence bond method we must write down those structures which correspond to the maximum number of bonds. Having done this we must then write down the spin eigenfunctions which have eigenvalues of S_z of zero. These functions are then arranged so as to give spin functions which correspond to the perfect pairing of the electrons in the structures written out. Having done this we then evaluate the matrix elements of the Hamiltonian between the various determinants which make up the wave functions of the individual structures. From these we construct the matrix elements corresponding to the individual structures and the interaction elements between them. The secular determinant is then solved in the usual manner and the wave function for the ground state evaluated.

Group theory may be used to simplify the elements. Structures which form bases for different representations of the point group will not interact and elements of the Hamiltonian will vanish.

One great drawback to this method of calculating molecular wave functions is that of enumerating the various structures which may occur. In benzene for example there are five structures, each corresponding to three double bonds, which must be included, whilst when we consider naphthalene it is found that no less than forty-two independent structures, each corresponding to five double bonds, may be constructed.

5. Resonance Energy

In many cases it is found that the only structures which have any significant weight in the ground state wave function are those which correspond to the maximum number of bonds. In many cases the wave function will indicate only one possible structure and the bonds are then localized. In aromatic and conjugated hydrocarbons, however, this is not so. We have seen that here the wave function for the ground state is a linear combination of structures which correspond to different pairings of the electrons. In the former case, where the ground state wave function can be represented by a single structure or single-bond eigenfunction ψ_A, the energy of the ground state is given by

$$E = H_{AA} \tag{24}$$

assuming that the ψ_A is normalized. H_{AA} must then be expanded in terms of the Coulomb integral Q and the exchange integrals (ab). This leads to the following expression for the energy

$$\begin{aligned} E = \quad & Q + \Sigma \quad \text{(exchange integrals between bonded orbitals)} \\ & -\tfrac{1}{2}\Sigma \quad \text{(exchange integrals between non-bonded orbitals)} \end{aligned}$$

When there are two or more structures which have the same energy or nearly the same energy the ground state wave function can be represented by none of these structures alone but by a linear combination of them all. These participating structures have been called "canonical structures" and the corresponding wave function, or structure derived from them, the "resonance state" or the "resonance hybrid". As we have already pointed out the canonical structures have no objective reality, the only structure which has any reality is the final state which is the result of mixing these structures.

When these structures are mixed, the resultant state has an energy which is lower than that of any of the contributory structures. This gain in energy is known as the resonance energy and is the analogue of the delocalization energy which arises in the molecular orbital theory of conjugated and aromatic hydrocarbons.

If we carry out a valence bond calculation on benzene using only the two Kekulé structures (see Fig. 12) we find that the resonance energy has a value 0·9α. If, however, we include the three Dewar structures (see Fig. 13) as well the resonance energy increases to 1·106α. In Table 9 we summarize the results for benzene.

TABLE 9. Resonance energy of benzene

Structures used	Wave function	Energy (α)	Resonance energy (α)
Single Kekulé	Ψ_k	$Q+1·5$	
Two Kekulé	$\Psi_{k1}+\Psi_{k2}$	$Q+2·4$	0·9
Single Dewar	Ψ_D	Q	
Three Dewar	$\Psi_{D1}+\Psi_{D2}+\Psi_{D3}$	$Q+2·0$	0·5*
Five structures	$C_1(\Psi_{k1}+\Psi_{k2})+C_2(\Psi_{D1}+\Psi_{D2}+\Psi_{D3})$	$Q+2·606$	1·106*

* These resonance energies are relative to the single Kekulé structures.

From the table it can be seen that the bulk of the resonance energy in benzene comes from the mixing of the two Kekulé-type structures. Inclusion of the three Dewar-type structures gives a gain of $0{\cdot}206\alpha$ or a gain of only 20% in the resonance energy. This small gain is due to the Kekulé and Dewar structures having different energies. From the table it is seen that the single Kekulé structure has an energy of $Q+1{\cdot}5\alpha$ whilst the single Dewar structure has an energy of $2{\cdot}0\alpha+Q$. When we examine the wave function it is seen that C_2/C_1 has the value 0·4341. The relative weights of each Dewar and Kekulé structure are then $0{\cdot}4341^2/1$ or 0·19:1. Each Kekulé structure then occurs with a weight five times that with which each Dewar structure occurs. To a good first approximation the benzene molecule can be described in terms of the two Kekulé-type structures.

When we look at the polyacene series, we quickly have to include a prohibitively large number of structures. Resonance energies for the first three members of the series calculated using the valence bond method are given in Table 10 together with the experimental resonance energies.

TABLE 10. Resonance energy of some polyacenes

Hydrocarbon	Calculated resonance energy (α)	Experimental resonance energy (kcal/mole)
Benzene	1·106	36·0
Naphthalene	2·040	61·0
Anthracene	2·951	83·5

This gives us a method of determining the value of exchange integral α. The ratios of calculated to experimental resonance energy in the three cases is 32·4, 30·0, and 28·3. This suggests a value for α of about 30 kcal/mole. One disturbing feature, however, is that the value of α appears to decrease with increasing number of rings. From an examination of the calculated resonance energies it can be seen that the resonance energy increases by about $0{\cdot}95\alpha$ per ring.

If this value of α is a consistent one it should be transferable to the open conjugated hydrocarbons. For butadiene and hexatriene it is found that the calculated resonance energies are 0·23 and $0{\cdot}48\alpha$ respectively. The observed value for butadiene is 3·5 kcal/mole and there is no value given in the literature for hexatriene. Using our value of 30 kcal/mole for α we predict a resonance energy of 7 kcal/mole for butadiene and hexatriene. Clearly for butadiene the prediction is out by a factor of two. As with molecular orbital delocalization energies, we find that we cannot obtain a consistent value of the exchange integral α in valence bond theory and β in molecular orbital theory.

One further interesting point arises if we compare the resonance energies of butadiene and hexatriene with their cyclic analogues cyclobutadiene and benzene. The resonance energies of cyclobutadiene and benzene are 1·0 and 1·106α respectively. The values for butadiene and hexatriene are 0·23 and 0·48α respectively. The cyclic structure clearly has a much greater resonance energy than its open chain analogue. When we write down the contributory structures for the two cases the reason becomes obvious. Whilst for the cyclic structure we can always write more than one structure with the maximum number of nearest bonds, for the open chain molecule there is only one structure which corresponds to the maximum number of nearest-neighbour bonds. Other structures for the open chain are analogous to the Dewar-type structures for benzene and consequently have a higher energy than that for the maximum nearest-neighbour structure. We are led to a general conclusion that the ground state of an open chain conjugated hydrocarbon can be described to a first approximation by a single structure containing the maximum number of nearest-neighbour bonds whilst the isoelectronic cyclic structure can only be described by a structure which is a linear combination of the several structures containing the maximum number of nearest-neighbour bonds.

It is now pertinent to ask why cyclobutadiene does not exist when it has a resonance energy of the same order as benzene. The reason for this can be seen when we think of the σ-bonded framework. The bond angles in cyclobutadiene must be 90° in the symmetrical structure. Since the normal bond angle for carbon in its sp_2-hybrid state is 120° it is easily seen that considerable distortion of these hybrid bonds must occur in the formation of cyclobutadiene. This distortion can only occur with considerable expense in terms of energy. This energy loss probably more than outweighs the gain in resonance energy and therefore the cyclobutadiene molecule is not stable.

6. Fractional Bond Order

In a conjugated or aromatic molecule there are no pure single or double bonds but all bonds lie someway between them. It is our task now to see if we can define a fractional bond order in the valence bond theory analogous to the π-bond order in the molecular orbital theory. This quantity may be obtained from a knowledge of the weight with which each structure occurs in the state wave function (Pauling, Brockway & Beach, 1935). Let us consider any of the bonds in benzene. It appears double in one or other of the two Kekulé structures and also in one of the three Dewar structures. Now the weight of each Kekulé structure in the wave function is 39% and the weight of each Dewar structure is 7%. The percentage double-bond character of the bond considered is 39 + 7 which is 46%. In this case all bonds have the same fractional bond character.

In the case of butadiene the fractional bond orders are 88% for the outer bonds and 12% for the inner bond. For naphthalene we find the following bond orders: 1–2 53%, 2–3 35%, 3–8 23% and 1–10 38% (the numbering of the atoms was shown in Fig. 5).

If we plot fractional bond order against bond length we find a curve similar to the one relating bond order in the MO theory to bond length.

7. Heterocyclic Molecules

In the molecular orbital theory of hetero-aromatic molecules the Coulomb integral α is replaced by $\alpha + \beta . \delta$, where the δ takes into account the difference in electronegativity between the heteroatom and the carbon atom. In the valence bond theory it is possible to include the effect of a heteroatom by the inclusion of ionic structures into the wave function for the ground state.

Consider pyridine. Pyridine can be considered formally as being derived from benzene by the simple replacement of one of the C—H groups by a nitrogen atom. This leaves the total number of π-electrons unchanged and the C—H bond is replaced by a lone-pair of electrons on the nitrogen atom. In addition to the five covalent structures considered for benzene we must consider ionic structures of which the most dominant ones are shown in Fig. 14.

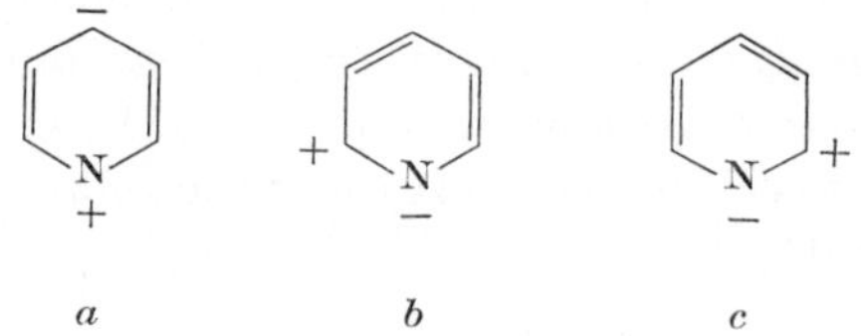

FIG. 14. Ionic structures for pyridine.

Inclusion of these three extra structures leads to a flow of electrons onto the nitrogen atom at the expense of the *ortho*- and *para*-carbon atoms. The *meta*-atoms are not affected in this, for the structure which we could draw in which an electron is transferred from a *meta*-atom to the nitrogen, makes it impossible to draw two other nearest-neighbour bonds. These structures then have a greater energy and can be ignored in first approximation.

There is nothing in principle to prevent us carrying through calculations on pyridine using the five purely covalent structures and these three ionic structures. All that remains to do is to evaluate a few Q's and α's. In practice, however, this is a very difficult task and the best way to determine their values is by appeal to experiment. If in the total wave function we represent the weights of the Kekulé and Dewar structures by w_k and w_a respectively and the weights of structures a, b and c in Fig. 14 by w_a and $w = w_b = w_c$, the charge on the nitrogen atom is

$$(w_a + 2w)/100$$

on each *ortho*-atom it is $w/100$ and on the *para*-atom $w_a/100$, when we write

$$2w_k + 3w_d + w_a + 2w = 100$$

The fractional bond orders will be $w_k + w_d$ for the C—N bond, $w_k + w_d + w_a + w$ for the *o–m* C—C bond and $w_k + w_d + w$ for the *m–p* C—C bond.

One way of determining the weights of the ionic structures would be to produce a charge distribution which is consistent with the dipole moment. Again we could use resonance energies, ionization potentials and spectra as alternative ways of determining the weights.

8. Odd-membered Ring Molecules

When we come to consider hydrocarbon molecules, which although possessing an even number of carbon atoms have odd-membered rings, we run into difficulties. Fulvene for example (see Fig. 15) has six carbon

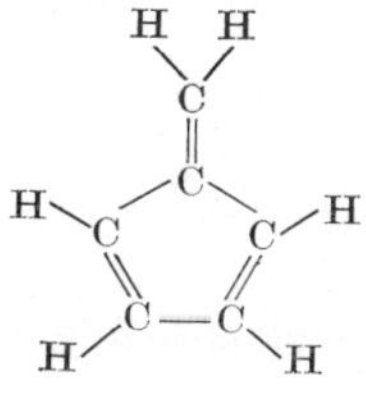

FIG. 15. The fulvene molecule.

atoms and six π-electrons. There is, however, only one Kekulé-type structure in which the six electrons are assigned to nearest-neighbour bonds. When we pass to structures containing only two nearest-neighbour bonds and one long "Dewar" bond, it is easily seen that five additional structures must be considered. These five structures are shown in Fig. 16.

The energy of the structure with three localized bonds is $Q+1\cdot5\alpha$. The energy of the ground state structure is found to be $Q+2\cdot0\alpha$. This gives a

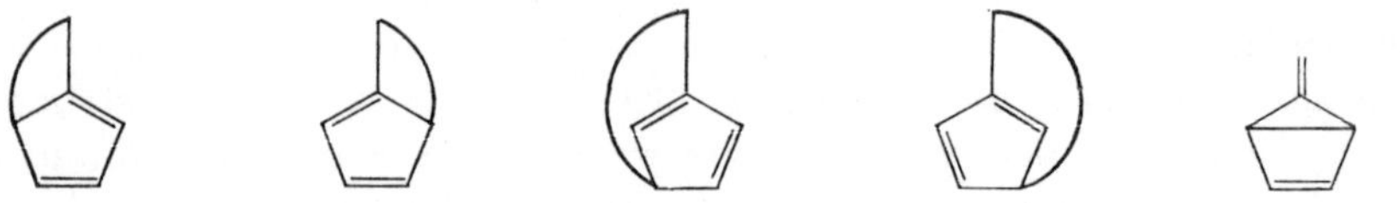

FIG. 16. Dewar structures for fulvene.

resonance energy of $0\cdot5\alpha$. The resonance energy for fulvene then is of the same order as that for hexatriene and about half that for benzene. As we noted for hexatriene so for fulvene, there is only one structure which corresponds to the maximum number of nearest-neighbour bonds.

The fractional bond character of the π-bonds in fulvene is shown in Fig. 17.

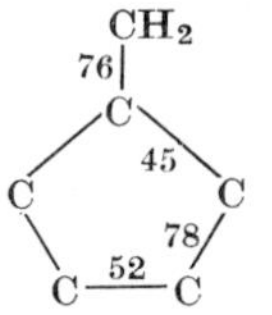

FIG. 17. Fractional bond orders for fulvene.

One molecule containing odd-membered rings which is of considerable interest is azulene. Azulene is isoelectronic with naphthalene but instead of two five-membered rings as in naphthalene, azulene has one seven-membered ring and one five-membered ring. The molecule is shown in Fig. 18. The dominating structures for azulene which each have five

FIG. 18. Kekulé structures for azulene.

nearest-neighbour bonds are both shown in Fig. 18. In addition to these structures of the Kekulé type we must also include several which have "Dewar" bonds, some of which are shown in Fig. 19.

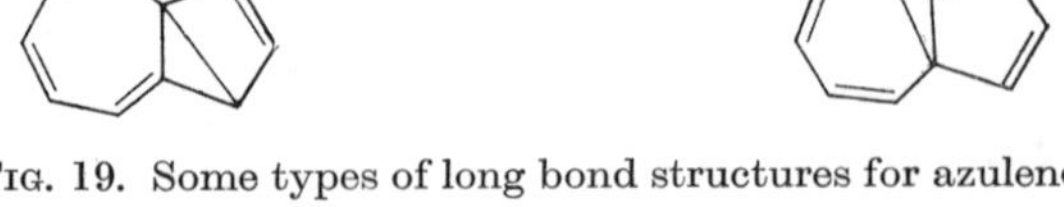

FIG. 19. Some types of long bond structures for azulene.

The resonance energy of the azulene molecule is found to be $1{\cdot}14\alpha$. The value given in Table 10 for naphthalene is $2{\cdot}04\alpha$. It is of interest to note that the resonance energy for azulene is only half that of the more stable naphthalene. This is also in agreement with the experimental values found for the resonance energy.

The fractional bond orders for the azulene molecule are shown in Fig. 20. Of considerable interest here is the bond order for the bond common to the two rings. This is almost a pure single bond.

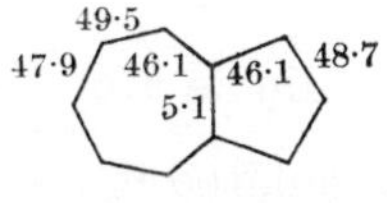

FIG. 20. Fractional bond orders for azulene.

It is of interest to compare these values of the resonance energy and the fractional bond orders with the corresponding values obtained in the Hückel molecular orbital theory. The resonance energy for fulvene is $1{\cdot}466\beta$ in the MO theory and $3{\cdot}364\beta$ for azulene. The corresponding values for the resonance energy of the isoelectronic species benzene and naphthalene are $2{\cdot}00\beta$ and $3{\cdot}683\beta$ respectively. It is clear that the Hückel MO theory predicts fulvene and azulene to be about as stable as benzene and naphthalene. This is in complete contradiction with both the valence bond theory and with the experimental data for azulene and fulvene. The charges and bond orders in the Hückel molecular orbital theory for fulvene and azulene are shown in Fig. 21. One interesting observation which arises from this is that the bond common to the two rings in azulene, whilst having the lowest bond order, does not have such a high single-bond character as it is given in the valence bond theory.

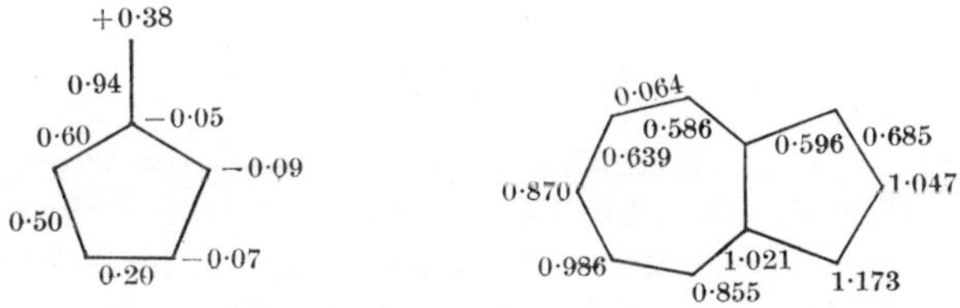

FIG. 21. MO charges and bond orders for fulvene and azulene.

Another interesting fact which can be seen from Fig. 21 is that the charge distribution in fulvene and azulene is not uniform. By exclusion of ionic structures the charge distribution in the valence bond theory is assumed to be uniform. In the MO theory fulvene and azulene are expected to have dipole moments of 4·7 D and 6·9 D respectively. Whilst experimental work certainly shows these molecules to possess dipole moments they are certainly a degree of magnitude smaller than those predicted by the MO theory, having the value 1·2 D for fulvene and 1·0 D for azulene. This is another indication of the well-known fact that molecular orbital theory over-emphasizes ionic character whilst valence bond theory considerably underestimates it. The valence bond theory of these molecules can only be improved by including some ionic structures in the calculation.

9. Dipole Moments

Dipole moments can be calculated in a straightforward manner in the valence bond theory. In Section 6 we discussed the calculation of the structure of heterocyclic molecules by including the appropriate ionic structures. A calculation based on a set including ionic structures and the variation of Q, to take into account the different electronegativity of the heteroatom, would then yield a dipole moment for the molecule. This could be one of the ways of determining the value of Q appropriate to the heteroatom.

To calculate the dipole moment it is only necessary to know the fractional charges on the atoms. This is readily determined once the weights of the contributing structures have been determined.

In the crude theory of aromatic hydrocarbons, which we have used to discuss the structures of fulvene and azulene, it is assumed that the Q's are independent of environment. That this assumption is untrue is shown by the fact that these molecules have substantial dipole moments. The presence of a dipole moment also indicates the error which occurs when ionic structures are ignored.

10. Free Valence

There are two alternative ways of defining the free valence in valence bond theory. The simpler definition assumes that any electron involved in a long "Dewar"-type bond is free to engage in bond formation with reacting species. Hence, in this definition, the free valence at an atom is the sum of the weights of the structures in which the given atom is involved in a long bond. In benzene for example, when only the Kekulé structures are considered, there are no long bonds and therefore the free valence for every atom is zero. When the three Dewar structures are included, each atom has a long bond attached to it in one of the Dewar structures, the free valence has the value 7, since each Dewar structure has a weight of 7% in the structure.

The alternative definition of F is analogous to that used in molecular orbital theory. The sum of the bond orders terminating on a given atom is subtracted from F_{max} and the resultant number is called the free valence of the atom considered. Using a value of 4·732 for F_{max} it is found that F for benzene has the value 0·812 when only Kekulé structures are included and the value 0·740 when Kekulé and Dewar structures are included.

The free valencies for the atoms of some hydrocarbons are given in Fig. 22 using the second definition.

FIG. 22. Free valence in valence bond theory.

11. Electronic Spectra

The molecular orbital theory, at least in its more simple form, provides a satisfactory qualitative picture of electronic excitation. An electron is considered to be promoted from an occupied orbital to an orbital which was previously empty. We saw in Chapter 2, however, that this simple picture of "electron jumps" is, on the whole, unsatisfactory when we seek a quantitative understanding of the excitation energies in the molecule. In order to obtain a more sophisticated model, we saw that it is necessary to introduce interaction between several configurations and also between these excited configurations and the ground state. When this is done the simple picture of an excitation being represented as a single "electron jump" is lost. We shall discuss a more sophisticated model using molecular orbital theory in a later chapter.

It is necessary to ask if any simple picture comes out of the valence bond theory to describe electronic excitations. This is desirable because of the chemical implications of the valence bond theory. Although no better than molecular orbital theory in trying to understand the structure and the properties of the ground state, the valence bond theory affords a straightforward, although naïve, understanding of chemist's empirical ideas on valence.

In seeking to understand the structure of an excited state in valence bond theory there are some molecules which present no problems. For example, in the case of ethylene where only two π-electrons are involved, the excited state can only be described in terms of the ionic structures which are normally omitted in valence bond theory. The excited state will be described by a function containing equal weights of the two possible ionic structures. The description here is completely analogous to the description of the first excited state of hydrogen (see Jaffe & Orchin, 1962, p. 170).

When we go to more complicated π-electron molecules the description is no longer straightforward. For butadiene we should have to use the structures which correspond to the higher energy states which arise out of the ground state problem and also the ionic states $C^+—C=C—C^-$, and $C^-—C=C—C^+$. As we go to even more complicated problems the number of structures which must be included becomes prohibitively large. It is for this reason that little work has been done on excited states using the valence bond theory.

One very important application of the theory is in understanding the behaviour of groups containing fixed double bonds on excitation. For example, the carbonyl group which is largely C=O in the ground state must contain a large weighting $C^-—O^+$ in the excited state. Where this type of ionic structure predominates in the excited state we can speak of an intramolecular charge-transfer spectrum. Since, however, the ground state function of the C=O is probably heavily weighted with the ionic structure $C^+—O^-$, the excited state structure perhaps goes no further than setting up a balance between the two ionic structures, yielding a structure which is to all intents and purposes covalent.

It is really our purpose to examine the structure of the excited states of aromatic and conjugated molecules. In describing the ground state we have used only covalent structures, both those containing only nearest-neighbour bonds and those containing the long "Dewar" bonds. It is a defect of the scheme that we have used that ionic structures have been largely ignored. In a more rigorous reformulation of the scheme we shall see that it is the ionic structures which lead to a stable molecule.

We are faced here with a dilemma when attempting to describe the excited states of our given molecule. Do we ignore the contributions of the ionic structures to the excited and use only the higher states which result from the ground state calculation, or do we use an extended basis set including ionic structures to calculate the excited states? Most calculations which have been carried through have included only purely covalent structures. Calculations on benzene and naphthalene have been carried through including ionic structures and we shall look at these in a little while.

Table 11 gives the values of the lowest electronic excitation energy for the first four members of the polyene series in which all non-ionic structures have been included.

From these values a value of the exchange integral α can be obtained. These values are shown in the fourth column of Table 11. The average

TABLE 11. Lowest bands for simple polyenes

	Calculated (α)	Observed ($\bar{\nu}$)	Observed / Calculated
Butadiene	3·46	46,080	13,300
Hexatriene	2·61	39,750	15,200
Octatetraene	2·07	33,300	16,000

value of α is found to be about $15{,}000\nu$ or 1·875 eV, which is approximately 43 kcal/mole. This is higher than the value obtained from resonance energy considerations which would have required a value of about 15 kcal/mole to fit the polyene data. One other disturbing feature is that the value of α increases with increasing chain length.

Consider now the values obtained for the polyacene series. Table 12 gives the values of the lowest bonds for each of the first five polyacenes calculated using only the Kekulé-type structures. The experimental values are also given together with the value of α derived from them for each hydrocarbon.

TABLE 12. Lowest bands for polyacenes

	Calculated	Observed	α
Benzene	2·40	37,900	16,000
Naphthalene	1·97	31,800	16,200
Anthracene	1·60	26,400	16,500
Naphthacene	1·31	21,200	16,200
Pentacene	1·08	17,400	16,200

The first point to note is that a consistent value for α is obtained from these data. Furthermore, the value is consistent for both the polyenes and the polyacenes. It should be remembered, however, that the value is certainly nothing like constant in the polyene series.

The values given in the table are all based only on Kekulé-type structures. It is necessary before proceeding any further to ask what is the effect of including firstly long bond structures and secondly ionic structures? Without knowledge of the effect of these two important factors we cannot place any real confidence in the results. The transition energy for the lowest excited state in benzene when the three Dewar structures are included is found to be $2{\cdot}61\alpha$. This is in fair agreement with the value obtained using only Kekulé structures. When the ionic structures are included with the Kekulé structures for naphthalene it is found that the transition energy corresponding to the lowest transition has the value

$2{\cdot}25\alpha$. Again this is in reasonable agreement with the transition energy for the Kekulé-type function alone. It may be concluded therefore that to a first approximation the lowest excited state can be described in terms of the Kekulé structures.

One other point is that the energy of the lowest transition decreases with increasing number of rings. From an examination of Table 12 it appears that the transition energy converges to a limit with increasing number of rings. We shall see later that this conclusion also applies in the molecular orbital theory when configuration interaction, together with proper inclusion of two-electron interaction terms, is used.

12. Alternative Evaluation of Matrix Elements

We have already met one easy method for writing down the energy of a single structure, i.e. the matrix element H_{AA} in Section 5. This is given by

$$H_{AA} = Q + \Sigma \text{ (exchange integrals between bonded orbitals)} - \tfrac{1}{2}\Sigma \text{ (exchange integrals between non-bonded orbitals)} \quad (25)$$

This may be rewritten in another way. Write down the structure under consideration, say one of the Kekulé structures for benzene. Draw it out again, this time omitting the σ-bonds. A diagram of the form

(a) (b)

results. Superpose this pattern upon itself and a pattern like b results. Each of these double lines is called an island. Such a pattern consists of a set of closed islands. In our example the number of islands, i, is 3. The element H_{AA} then has the value

$$H_{AA} = \frac{1}{2^{N-i}}(Q + b\alpha) \quad (26)$$

where $2N$ is the total number of electrons, Q and α are the usual Coulomb and exchange integrals and b is a quantity which is given by the number of pairs of nearest neighbours in the islands of the superposition pattern minus one-half times the number of nearest-neighbour orbitals on separate islands.

In our example 2^{N-i} has the value unity since $N = 3$ and $i = 3$. b has the value $3-\frac{1}{2}.3$, i.e. 1·5. The energy of a single Kekulé structure in benzene then is $Q+1{\cdot}5\alpha$. For a single Dewar structure the superposition pattern will be

From this it can be seen that 2^{N-i} is again unity and b has the value $2-\frac{1}{2}.4$, i.e. the energy of a single Dewar structure is Q. These values are in agreement with those found by the more fundamental method given earlier.

We must now seek a similar method for writing down the off-diagonal elements of the Hamiltonian between the various structures. A similar formula applies. We write down the diagram which corresponds to the π-bonds in each structure and then write down a diagram in which one diagram is superposed on the other. Again a set of islands results, and the element of H corresponding to the two structures is given by

$$H_{rs} = \frac{1}{2^{N-i}}(Q+b\alpha) \tag{27}$$

where N and i are defined as before and b is the number of nearest-neighbour orbitals (whether bonded or not) in the islands of the superposition pattern minus one-half the number of nearest-neighbour pairs on separate islands.

We shall calculate the off-diagonal elements of H between (*a*) the two Kekulé structures for benzene, (*b*) one Kekulé and one Dewar structure and (*c*) two Dewar structures.

The superposition patterns for the three terms are

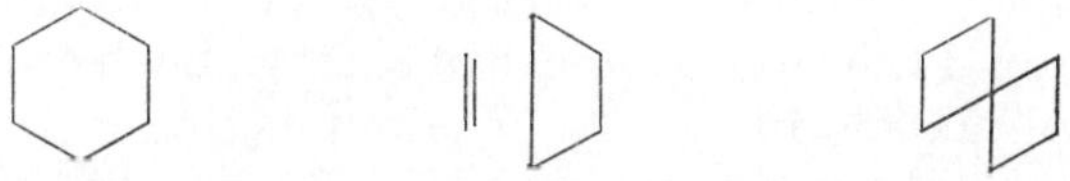

a *b* *c*

(*a*) Two Kekulé, (*b*) one Kekulé and one Dewar, (*c*) two Dewar.

Using equation (27) and the diagrams (*a*), (*b*), (*c*), it is easily seen that H_{rs} between the two Kekulé structures has the value $4^{-1}(Q+6\alpha)$, between one Kekulé and one Dewar structure the value $\frac{1}{2}(Q+3\alpha)$ and between two Dewar structures the value $4^{-1}(Q+8\alpha)$.

It only remains now to evaluate the overlap integrals between the various structures. The modulus of the overlap integral is equal to the coefficient of Q, both for the diagonal elements and for the off-diagonal elements. Multiplication through by the appropriate factors can put each element into the form assumed when the basis structures form a normalized set. The sign of S is the same as the sign for Q. For a diagonal element this is simple to take care of for the overlap integral is always a positive number. For the off-diagonal elements of H, however, this is not the case and the elements of H calculated using (27) may be wrong by a factor of -1, after normalization problems have been taken care of. The overlap integral must then be evaluated in order to determine the sign of the element resulting from (27).

The discussion which we have given here is essentially that given by Pauling (1933), which should be consulted in order to see under what circumstances the off-diagonal should be multiplied by -1.

One simplification often used for large molecules, is to assume that each Kekulé structure has the same energy, and similarly the energy of every structure in a given category will by the same. Furthermore, off-diagonal elements of the same type will be identical. This often reduces the labour considerably and makes problems tractable which otherwise would be extremely tedious to solve.

13. Enumeration of Canonical Structures

If an extensive valence bond calculation is envisaged, it is necessary to have some way of generating a set of canonical structures according to some system or logic. One possibility would be to write down all those structures which represented the maximum number of bonds including long bonds. We should then be compelled to ask if such a set was complete or perhaps if the set was over-complete?

Rumer (1932) has shown that in fact a set enumerated in this way would be grossly over-complete. Rumer gives a method whereby the necessary complete set can be generated. The atoms forming the molecule are written around the circumference of a circle. Such an arrangement is shown for naphthalene in Fig. 23. The numbering of the atoms is immaterial to the method. If there are $2N$ atoms, i.e. $2N$ π-electrons, then

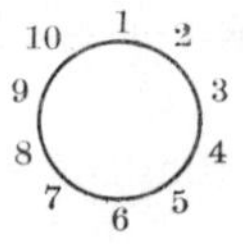

FIG. 23.

we start drawing the structures which contain N bonds. It does not matter whether these bonds link different sorts of atoms, the only restriction is that the line joining any two atoms in the diagram should not cross any other line joining any other of the N – 2 pairs of atoms in the structure. Having exhausted the possibilities of N bonds the whole procedure is repeated for $N-1$ bonds and so on until we arrive at the single structure which contains no bonds. When we have been through this whole procedure we have generated the complete set of structures in which only non-polar structures are included. Such sets of diagrams are known as Rumer diagrams.

In Fig. 24 we draw the possible Rumer diagrams for benzene with three bonds. There are five structures which contain three bonds, six structures corresponding to two bonds and six structures corresponding to one bond, and finally one structure corresponding to no bonds.

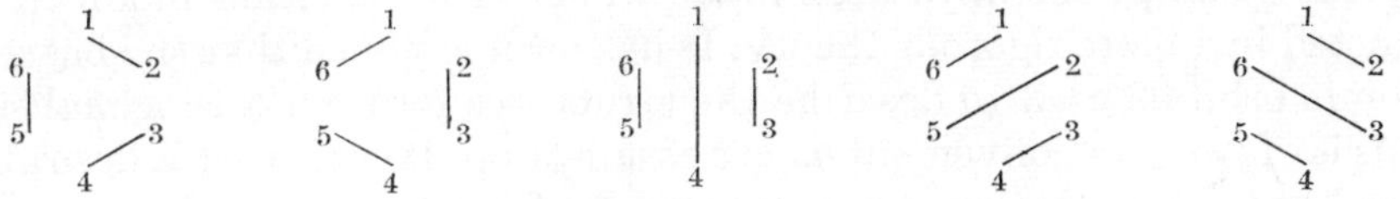

FIG. 24. Rumer diagrams for benzene.

The most important subset is of course that set which corresponds to the maximum number of bonds. In the Rumer method of generating this set it is not necessary to distinguish between nearest-neighbour bonds and non-nearest neighbour bonds. This difference only becomes relevant when evaluating the matrix element.

Any structure which contains "crossed" bonds can be represented as a linear combination of structures which contain no crossed bonds.

The number of structures which contain the maximum number of bonds is given by

$$\frac{N!}{(N/2)!\,(N/2+1)!} \tag{28}$$

where N is the total number of electrons (which must be even). These are the only structures which will combine to give functions whose spin parts are eigenfunctions of S^2 with eigenvalue zero.

This method of generating structures has considerable advantages over the method given at the beginning of this chapter to generate such bond eigenfunctions. The difficulty in that case was that firstly it was necessary to write down all of the spin functions with S_z values of zero. Secondly, bond eigenfunctions had to be constructed out of them and finally it was necessary to check that such functions were indeed eigenfunctions of S^2. The number of structures with the maximum number of bonds is always considerably smaller than the total number of spin functions. Since we have alternative methods of evaluating the matrix elements we no longer need to have any explicit knowledge of the spin eigenfunctions corresponding to the maximum bond structures. For example, in the cyclobutadiene problem which we considered in detail, whilst there are six spin functions to be considered, in fact there are only two independent structures which contain two bonds.

Using Rumer diagrams, equation (28) and the equations for the matrix elements (26) and (27), it is possible to at least formulate the secular determinant with little difficulty.

14. Improvements in the Theory

In the valence bond theory as we have developed it in this chapter several assumptions have been made which must be either modified or omitted in a more rigorous theory. It has been assumed that the basis of atomic orbitals used to describe the structures form an orthogonal set. This is of course a convenient *ad hoc* assumption. If such a set is desirable then they should be constructed properly from the non-orthogonal set of ordinary atomic orbitals.

It has also been assumed that the π-electrons move independently of each other, and all two-body interactions involving these electrons have been set equal to zero. Clearly an improved theory would include these integrals in the Hamiltonian. This is analogous to the technique suggested in the last chapter for the improvement of the Hückel model in molecular orbital theory.

To obtain a quantitative valence bond theory it is obvious that more structures ought to be included. It is clearly insufficient to use a basis set which is truncated to those structures which have the maximum number of double bonds. Structures containing fewer bonds and polar structures must be included in the basis set if a quantitative theory is to be set up. Whilst the valence bond theory and molecular orbital theory are equivalent when the complete set of functions is used in each case and when the two-electron interactions are properly evaluated in each case, in practice these conditions are extremely difficult if not impossible to satisfy in any interesting cases.

When the basic integrals are evaluated certain disturbing features emerge. In the case of a hydrogen molecule Slater (1951) has shown that when overlap is neglected the exchange integral α has a positive value. Overlap must be included in the calculation of α to obtain a negative value. McWeeny (1954) has shown that in the case of a hydrogen molecule use of a basis set of orbitals which are orthogonal leads to the paradox that the formally "covalent" structure corresponds to strong repulsion between the bonded atoms. The high charge density between the atoms and the bonding which results thereby arises when the wave function contains pairs of structures which show a "hop" between the atoms. In a valence bond theory founded on a basis of atomic orbitals which are rigorously orthogonal, bonding is a result of interconfigurational effects. Conventional valence bond structures have been shown (McWeeny, 1954b) to be equivalent to certain groupings of structures in the orthogonal basis. These groupings contain both polar and non-polar terms. The whole theory of spin-pairing, when formulated in terms of these orthogonal AO valence bond structures, is without foundation.

In a third paper in the series McWeeny (1955) applies the rigorous valence bond theory using orthogonalized basis orbitals to cyclobutadiene and benzene. For butadiene he uses complete sets of all non-polar, singlet and triplet structures. For benzene he uses 89 singlet and 69 triplet structures from the complete sets of 175 singlet and 189 triplet structures. One of the surprising results of this work is that doubly polar structures have a quite unexpected importance. From an examination of his energy levels it can be seen that inclusion of doubly polar structures causes very significant depressions in the ground state. The first two electronic transitions lead to states which have the symmetry ${}^1B_{2u}$ and ${}^1E_{2g}$ (if we ignore the two triplet states which are sandwiched between them). This gives transition energies of 2·5 eV and 4·75 eV for the first two singlet transitions. Many molecular orbital calculations predict the second singlet state to have the symmetry B_{1u}. This prediction, using the valence bond theory, agrees with the molecular orbital calculations of Parr, Craig & Ross (1950).

It can be seen that even a most sophisticated form of the theory in which large numbers of structures are included give relatively unsatisfactory results. McWeeny's excited state energies for benzene are in error by about 2 eV for each of the lowest two states. To carry through calculations including even more structures would not be a realistic proposition.

When the empirical nature and significance of the traditional valence bond structures is lost there seems little point in developing further a method which is already rather clumsy in its formulation. In what follows we shall deal exclusively with orbital theories. Before leaving the valence bond theory it is, however, necessary to emphasize again that in the limit when all structures can be included, the valence bond theory is identical to the molecular orbital approach when the complete set of configurations is included.

References

Jaffe, H. H. & Orchin, M. (1962). "Theory and Applications of Ultraviolet Spectroscopy." John Wiley and Sons Inc., New York.

McWeeny, R. (1954a). *Proc. R. Soc.* **A223**, 63.

McWeeny, R. (1954b). *Proc. R. Soc.* **A223**, 306.
McWeeny, R. (1955). *Proc. R. Soc.* **A227**, 288
Parr, R. G., Craig, D. P. & Ross, I. G. (1950). *J. chem. Phys.* **18**, 1561.
Pauling, L. (1933). *J. chem. Phys.* **1**, 280.
Pauling, L., Brockway, L. O. & Beach, J. Y. (1935). *J. Am. chem. Soc.* **57**, 2705.
Rumer, G. (1932). *Gottingen Nachr.* 377.
Slater, J. C. (1951). *J. chem. Phys.* **19**, 220.

CHAPTER 4

Improved Hückel Models

1. Introduction

In Chapter 2 the Hückel model for aromatic and conjugated hydrocarbons was discussed in detail. It was seen that the results of this simplified molecular orbital theory when applied to physical properties was disappointing. The parameters α and β do not have values which are transferable from either one molecule to another or which predict different electronic properties of the same molecules with any degree of accuracy.

In seeking to improve the model there are several changes which can be made. It is physically realistic as well as convenient to retain the one-electron model; that is, writing the total molecular wave function as an antisymmetrized product of one-electron orbitals. Further, it is convenient to retain the LCAO approximation in which each one of these one-electron molecular orbitals is expanded as a linear combination of atomic orbitals having coefficients determined by the variational procedure. The main sources of improvement are then:

(*a*) Variation of the parameters α and β, to reflect changes in environment.

(*b*) To introduce explicitly into the Hamiltonian the two-electron interaction terms between the π-electrons.

In this chapter we shall be concerned with the first of these. The use of a Hamiltonian in which the two-electron interactions are properly included will be our concern in the later chapters.

Firstly, however, it is necessary to discuss the inclusion of overlap in our calculations.

2. Hückel Theory with Overlap

The form taken by the off-diagonal elements on the secular determinant when a basis of non-orthogonal AOs is used is

$$h_{rs} = H_{rs} - E_{rs} S_{rs} \tag{1}$$

For carbon $2p_z$ atomic orbitals at an internuclear distance of 1·40 Å (the average "bond length" in an aromatic hydrocarbon) the overlap integral has a value of about 0·25. Since E usually has values of the order of unity (in units of β), it is easily seen that such terms cannot be ignored. Either we must recognize that we are working in a basis of rigorously orthogonal atomic orbitals or else we must include the overlap terms properly.

If we are to assume that our basis set is rigorously orthogonal then certain consequences must be faced. The basis orbitals are now linear combinations of the ordinary $2p_z$-orbitals and these orthogonal orbitals will no longer be localized. Further, except in a few fortuitous cases, the orthogonalized orbitals will not be centrosymmetric. This being the case it is clearly improper to call the P_{ii} the π-electron charge on atom i or to say that $2P_{ij}$ is proportional to the charge in the bond i—j. The full significance of these quantities and their relation to the charges and bond orders will be discussed in a later chapter.

If overlap is included then it is convenient to define a new quantity (Mulliken, Rieke & Brown, 1941)

$$\gamma = \beta - S\alpha \tag{2}$$

where S is taken to be zero except for nearest neighbours. This is a justifiable assumption since S for second neighbours has the value of about 0·03. Making the usual assumptions about H_{rs}, i.e. it has the value β for nearest neighbours and zero otherwise, the expression for the off-diagonal elements of the Hamiltonian h_{rs} become

$$h_{rs} = \beta - ES = \gamma + S(\alpha - E) \tag{3}$$

for nearest neighbours and zero otherwise.

The secular determinant then has the form

$$\begin{vmatrix} (\alpha-E) & \gamma+S(\alpha-E) & 0 & 0 \\ \gamma+S(\alpha-E) & (\alpha-E) & \gamma+S(\alpha-E) & 0 \\ 0 & \gamma+S(\alpha-E) & (\alpha-E) & \gamma+S(\alpha-E) \\ 0 & 0 & \gamma+S(\alpha-E) & (\alpha-E) \end{vmatrix} = 0 \tag{4}$$

for butadiene.

For computational purposes further simplifications can be made. A quantity x may be defined by

$$x = (\alpha - E)/\gamma \tag{5}$$

The diagonal elements for a hydrocarbon then have the value x and the off-diagonal elements the value $1+Sx$. A further step is then to write $b = 1+Sx$. The secular determinant now has the form

$$\begin{vmatrix} x & b & 0 & 0 \\ b & x & b & 0 \\ 0 & b & x & b \\ 0 & 0 & b & x \end{vmatrix} = 0 \tag{6}$$

The roots of the determinant have the form

$$x_i = -m_i b = -m_i(1+Sx_i) \tag{7}$$

which on substitution for x_i gives

$$E_i = \alpha + \frac{m_i}{1+m_i S}\gamma \tag{8}$$

Following Wheland (1941) we can write

$$n_i = \frac{m_i}{1+m_i S}$$

which gives

$$E_i = \alpha + n_i \gamma \tag{9}$$

Whilst changes of this nature lead to a different distribution of charge density in the molecule, it is found that they have very little effect on delocalization energies and total π-electron energies. There is a significant change in the spacing of energy levels but radical differences in the spacing of the spectral levels does not occur.

In conclusion we may say that although it is more rigorous to include overlap, it is found that no improvement occurs in the results obtained using the improved model.

McWeeny (1951) and Peacock (1959) have shown how charges and bond orders calculated in an orthogonal basis may be converted into those in the basis of non-orthogonal orbitals. In view of this it seems tedious to carry through the calculations in the orthogonal basis. Further discussion of this matter will be deferred until we discuss ground state properties in the self-consistent field approximation.

3. The Variation of β

One of the assumptions made in the Hückel approximation is that the resonance integral β between nearest-neighbour atoms has a constant value and for non-nearest neighbours has the value zero. This is tantamount to saying that all of the bond lengths are equal in such molecules. This is of course untrue and any improved scheme, even in the Hückel framework, will have to allow variation of β with bond length.

Lennard-Jones (1937) suggested that β was related to the bond energy and using a parabolic potential and measured force constants was able to calculate β for a pure single and a pure double bond. These values were clearly not correct and Mulliken *et al.* (1941) suggested that β_{rs} for bond r—s is related to β_0 for a standard bond length (1·397 Å) by the following relation

$$\beta_{rs} = k_{rs}\beta_0 \tag{10}$$

where k_{rs} is a dimensionless number. Dewar & Schmeising (1959) have given values for β which are larger than those obtained by Mulliken *et al.* The values for k vary from 1·71 for a bond length of 1·20 Å to 0·57 for a bond length of 1·54 Å.

Mulliken (1949) showed that β is proportional to the overlap integral S over the bond length distances which we are concerned with. If β_0 is defined for the standard bond length 1·397 Å, then β_{rs} for a bond rs is given by

$$\beta_{rs} = \beta_0 S_{rs}/S_0 \tag{11}$$

Mulliken's approximation works very well for diatomics over the range of values of interest and there is every reason to expect that values obtained for our β by this approximation will be reasonable.

One consequence of this relationship is that we can discuss the variation of β for p-orbitals which are twisted with respect to each other. Simonetta & Winstein (1954) have suggested the relationship

$$\frac{\beta}{\beta_0} = \frac{S/(1+S)}{S_0/(1+S_0)} \tag{12}$$

The simpler relationship

$$\beta = \beta_0 \cos\theta \tag{13}$$

has been used extensively by several writers and is due to Dewar (1952).

Several interesting studies have recently been made on the polyenes. If all resonance integrals are assumed to have the same value then the energy of the lowest unoccupied orbital and of the highest occupied molecular orbital both approach α as the chain length is increased, until in the limit when the chain length is infinite they both have the value α. In the simple Hückel model the energy of the lowest ultra-violet band of the polyenes should then approach zero as the chain length approaches infinity. However, it is found that there is a convergence limit.

If bond length alternation is admitted, i.e. bonds 1–2, 3–4... have the same value (r_1 say) and bonds 2–3, 4–5, etc. have the same value (r_2 say) and the β are adjusted accordingly, it is found that the lowest band of the spectrum converges to a limit which is not zero. Furthermore it is found that polyenes having bond alternation are more stable than those in which all of the bonds are equivalent.

Longuet-Higgins & Salem (1959) were the first authors to discuss this problem in detail. They assumed that the relation between bond length and π-bond order P is given by

$$r = 1{\cdot}50 - 0{\cdot}15P \tag{14}$$

where r is measured in Ångströms. The resonance integral was assumed to vary with r in the following fashion

$$\beta = -B\exp(-r/a) \tag{15}$$

where B and a are both constants. Longuet-Higgins and Salem deduced that for a large cyclic polyene the stable state is that in which the bonds alternate having lengths 1·4227 Å and 1·3872 Å respectively. The energies of the molecular orbitals instead of forming one large bond (as occurs with equal bond lengths) fall into two bands as follows

$$\left.\begin{array}{ll}\beta_1+\beta_2 \leqslant \epsilon < -\beta_1+\beta_2 & \text{(bonding)} \\ \beta_1-\beta_2 < \epsilon \leqslant -\beta_1-\beta_2 & \text{(antibonding)}\end{array} \quad (\beta_1 < \beta_2)\right\} \tag{16}$$

Similar conclusions for the open polyenes were reached by Tsugi, Huzinaga & Hasino (1960).

Coulson & Anno (1961) considered graphite as an aromatic molecule with infinite length in all directions. They looked for bond alternation in this case but found that the most stable state for graphite is that in which all of the bond lengths are equivalent.

In order to see the effect of the variation of β with bond length on the orbital energies we shall look at the solution of the butadiene problem. The outer C—C bonds in butadiene have a bond length of 1·34 Å and the inner bond a length of 1·48 Å. From what has gone before we find that the relevant values for β are $1{\cdot}1\beta_0$ and $0{\cdot}9\beta_0$ for the outer and inner bonds respectively. The secular determinant then has the form

$$\begin{vmatrix} (\alpha-E) & 1{\cdot}9\beta & 0 & 0 \\ 1{\cdot}1\beta & (\alpha-E) & 0{\cdot}9\beta & 0 \\ 0 & 0{\cdot}9\beta & (\alpha-E) & 1{\cdot}1\beta \\ 0 & 0 & 1{\cdot}1\beta & (\alpha-E) \end{vmatrix} = 0 \tag{17}$$

This determinant has eigenvalues $\alpha \pm 1{\cdot}64\beta$ and $\alpha \pm 0{\cdot}74\beta$. These compare with $\alpha \pm 1{\cdot}618\beta$ and $\alpha \pm 0{\cdot}618\beta$, when the βs are assumed to be equal. The total energy is found to be $4\alpha+4{\cdot}76\beta$ compared with $4\alpha+4{\cdot}472\beta$ with equal βs. It can be seen that the differences are sufficiently large to be significant.

Even after the introduction of the variation of β with bond length the orbitals still retain the properties of an alternant hydrocarbon. In other words the bonding and antibonding orbital energies are still symmetrical about α, the charge distribution is uniform, and the orbital coefficients in the related orbitals are still related in the same way as before. It will be seen that the properties of alternants originally defined in the framework of the Hückel model go over into self-consistent field model, where the two-electron interactions are properly included and where there are off-diagonal terms in the Hamiltonian corresponding to interactions between electrons in orbitals which are non-nearest neighbours.

Even, however, when the Hückel model is improved by inclusion the variation of β with bond length as discussed above the model is still unsatisfactory. One further improvement in the simple model is to allow α to vary with the molecular environment.

4. The Variation of α

In the last section the variation of β with bond length was considered. It is now necessary to consider the variation of α. To a first approximation it may be thought that in a conjugated hydrocarbon, α will have a different value depending upon whether the carbon atom has one, two or three other carbon atoms as nearest neighbours—in other words whether the carbon atom is the terminal atom in an open chain, an inner atom in an open chain which will be equivalent to a peripheral carbon atom in a condensed ring aromatic, or a "bridge" carbon atom as occurs for example with the central carbon atoms in naphthalene. Mulliken (1949) estimates that the α for a carbon atom may differ by about 1 eV depending upon whether the carbon atom is in benzene or ethylene.

One interesting method for taking the variation of α into account is the ω-technique which has been used extensively by Streitweiser in recent years (see, for example, Streitweiser, 1961, p. 115). This method faces the fact that a carbon atom in a lattice where the charges are not all unity cannot possibly have all of the α's having the same value. If $P_{rr} < 1$, the net positive charge means that this ion appears to be less screened by core electrons than if the π-charge was unity, and similarly if $P_{rr} > 1$ the ion appears to have a greater than normal electronic screening. It follows from this that α will have a more negative and a less negative value in the two cases respectively, compared with the "neutral" atom in the lattice. Wheland & Mann (1949) suggested that α is proportional to the net charge, viz.

$$\alpha_r = \alpha_0 + (1 - P_{rr})\,\omega\beta_0 \qquad (18)$$

The quantity ω is a dimensionless parameter chosen so as to agree with experiment. The experimental data commonly used to determine the value of ω is the dipole moment. The principal application of this technique has been with hydrocarbons and hydrocarbon ions. The values suggested for the parameter ω have varied between 0·33 and 1·08, although a substantial body of work by Streitweiser and others has arrived at a value of 1·4.

The process is an iterative one. From a first charge distribution a set of values for the α is calculated. From these a new charge distribution is calculated after solving the secular determinant. The whole process is then repeated until self-consistency is achieved between the charge distribution of the set of α values. In order to see the effect of these changes on the charge distribution we shall consider the allyl cation.

According to the ordinary Hückel theory the charges on the carbon atoms are 0·500 and 1·000 respectively. When self-consistency is achieved the charge distribution is found to be 0·571 and 0·858. The changes which occur are obviously very significant. At first sight this method yields improved results but as we shall see this sort of treatment presents grave difficulties which lead to conclusions which cannot be substantiated.

A similar sort of approach was suggested by Wheland & Pauling (1935) in dealing with heterocyclics. They sought to give mathematical interpretation to the so-called "inductive effect" well known to organic chemists. The more electronegative atom is considered to polarize the attached σ-bonds thus increasing the effective electronegativity of the adjacent carbon atoms. This has the effect of changing the α for the nearest-neighbour carbon atoms from α to $\alpha+\delta.\beta$. Various values for δ have been suggested. Wheland and Pauling suggested the value 0·1. The spread in values used ranges from 0·125 to 0·333. Later authors have suggested varying the next but one Coulomb integrals to take into account the inductive effect here.

This is in fact the difficulty about such a rule of thumb method. Having introduced an inductive parameter at what stage is it logical to stop the process? Indeed, one can easily finish with a large number of parameters to which any experimental data can be made to fit. This whole process of arbitrarily assigning these auxiliary inductive parameters has been severely criticized by McWeeny (1956) and McWeeny & Peacock (1957) who have shown that the assumptions cannot be justified.

We have discussed the variation of the parameters α and β with environment. Even including the changes suggested here the theory is still far from satisfactory. The theory can only be put on a satisfactory basis when interactions between the π-electrons are properly allowed. The Hamiltonian must be defined so that the π-electrons move in a field of tightly bound σ-electrons and the effective Hamiltonian calculated. The interactions between the π-electrons must then be included. In an ideal scheme the "core" Hamiltonian would be calculated using non-empirical methods; the two-electron interaction integrals would also be evaluated properly and a molecular self-consistent field calculation carried through as discussed in Chapter 1. An alternative is to calculate some of the terms and to choose others by appeal to experiment. We shall see later that this semi-empirical self-consistent field theory has had considerable success when applied to conjugated and aromatic molecules.

Before discussing the self-consistent field theory we shall consider the methods available for obtaining Hückel-type solutions for a molecule which differs only slightly from one whose solution is known. An example of this would be the pyridine molecule which differs from benzene by the substitution of a nitrogen atom for the C—H group. Another example is the formation of the diphenyl molecule from two benzene rings by forming a C—C bond in place of two hydrogen atoms which are removed. An obvious starting point here is the solution of the benzene molecule and introduce the extracyclic bond between the rings as a perturbation. Here we have an example of the two kinds of perturbation which we meet, the one where the Coulomb integral changes by a small amount δx, i.e. $\alpha \to \alpha + \delta\alpha$, and secondly where the resonance integral changes, in this case from zero to $\delta\beta$, or from $\beta \to \beta + \delta\beta$.

There are two theories which we shall use to discuss these effects. The first is a perturbation theory which was developed by Coulson & Longuet-Higgins (1947) and the second a "steepest descents" method which was formulated by McWeeny (1956a,b).

5. The Perturbation Method

Assume that the molecular orbitals for a given molecule are known. The energy of the system can then be written

$$E = 2\left(\sum_{rJ} c_{rJ}^2 \alpha + \sum_{\substack{r,sJ \\ r \neq s}} c_{rJ} c_{sJ} \beta_{rs}\right) \Big/ \sum_{rJ} c_{rJ}^2 \tag{19}$$

where r and s are coefficients of the atomic orbital ϕ_r and ϕ_s in the molecular orbital ψ_J.

The total energy can be expressed as

$$E = 2E_A + 2E_B + \ldots \tag{20}$$

where the E_J are the orbital energies.

The orbital energy E_J can be expressed in terms of the coefficients of the ϕs in the MO ψ_J

$$E_J = \left(\sum_{r} c_{rJ}^2 \alpha + \sum_{\substack{r,s \\ r \neq s}} c_{rJ} c_{sJ} \beta_{rs}\right) \Big/ \sum_{r} c_{rJ}^2 \tag{21}$$

If the atomic orbital basis is an orthonormal one, then

$$\sum_r c_{rJ}^2 = 1$$

and (21) becomes

$$E_J = \sum_r c_{rJ}^2 \alpha + \sum_{\substack{r,s \\ r \neq s}} c_{rJ} c_{sJ} \beta_{rs} \tag{22}$$

Let $\alpha_r \to \alpha + \delta\alpha_r$ and $\beta_{rs} \to \beta + \delta\beta_{rs}$, then change δE_J in E_J as from (22) given by

$$\delta E_J = \sum_r c_{rJ}^2 \delta\alpha + \sum_{\substack{r,s \\ r \neq s}} c_{rJ} c_{sJ} \delta\beta_{rs} + \sum_r \delta c_{rJ} \frac{\partial E_J}{\partial c_{rJ}} \tag{23}$$

Since $\partial E_J/\partial c_{rs} = 0$ (from variation theory), then

$$\delta E_J = \sum_r c_{rJ}^2\,\delta\alpha_r + \sum_{\substack{r,s\\ r\neq s}} c_{rJ}\,c_{sJ}\,\delta\beta_{rs} \tag{24}$$

This is true for small changes in α and β.

The orbital energies can also be obtained by direct solution of the secular determinant, and the derivative $(\partial E_J/\partial\alpha_r)_{\Delta=0}$ can be written down (Δ is the value of the secular determinant). Also

$$\left(\frac{\partial E_J}{\partial\alpha_r}\right)_{\Delta=0} = c_{rJ}^2\left(\frac{\partial E_J}{\partial\beta_{rs}}\right)_{\Delta=0} = 2c_{rJ}\,c_{rJ}$$

Summing over all occupied orbitals gives

$$P_{rr} = 2\sum_{J=1}^{M} c_{rJ}^2 = 2\sum_{J-1}^{M}\left(\frac{\partial E_J}{\partial\alpha_r}\right)_{\Delta=J} = \left(\frac{\partial E}{\partial\alpha_r}\right)_{\Delta=0} \tag{25}$$

and

$$P_{rs} = 2\sum_{J=1}^{M} c_{rJ}\,c_{sJ} = \sum_{J=1}^{M}\left(\frac{\partial E_J}{\partial\beta_{rs}}\right)_{\Delta=0} = \frac{1}{2}\left(\frac{\partial E}{\partial\beta_{rs}}\right)_{\Delta=0} \tag{26}$$

The charges and bond orders are then related to the change in total energy with variation on α and β respectively.

A. Perturbation $\delta\alpha_r$ in Element h_{rr}

The energy change can be expanded in a Taylor series about E_0 and we obtain

$$\partial E = \frac{\partial E}{\partial\alpha_r}\,\partial\alpha_r + \frac{1}{2}\frac{\partial^2 E}{\partial\alpha_r}\,\partial\alpha_r^2 + \ldots \tag{27}$$

Now $\partial E/\partial\alpha_r = P_{rr}$ and $\partial^2 E/\partial\alpha_r^2$ is defined as the self-polarizability $\pi_{rr,r}$ of atom r. Equation (27) then becomes

$$\partial E = P_{rr}\,\delta\alpha_r + \tfrac{1}{2}\pi_{rr,rr}\,\delta\alpha_r^2 \tag{28}$$

Coulson and Longuet-Higgins showed that these polarizabilities can be expressed in terms of the orbital coefficients.

$$\pi_{rr,rr} = 4\sum_{J=1}^{M}\sum_{K=M+1}^{N}\frac{c_{rJ}^2\,c_{rK}^2}{E_J - E_K} \tag{29}$$

where molecular orbital 1 to M are those which are occupied in the ground state and orbitals $M+1$ to N are those which are normally unoccupied.

Similar expressions can be obtained for the changes which occur in the charges and bond orders due to a perturbation $\delta\alpha_r$ in h_{rr}. The change in P_{rr} will be

$$\delta P_{rr} = \frac{\partial P_{rr}}{\partial \alpha_r}\delta\alpha_r = \pi_{rr,rr}\,\delta\alpha_r \tag{30}$$

whilst the change δP_{ss} due to the perturbation $\delta\alpha_r$ is

$$\delta P_{ss} = \pi_{ss,rr}\,\delta\alpha_r \tag{31}$$

where $\pi_{ss,rr}$ is known as the mutual atom polarizability, and is given by $\partial^2 E/\delta\alpha_r\,\partial\alpha_s$.

The effect on the bond order P_{st} of the perturbation is given by

$$\delta P_{st} = \pi_{st,rr}\delta\alpha_r \tag{32}$$

where $\pi_{st,rr}$ is the bond-atom polarizability. This is given by $\partial^2 E/\partial\alpha_r\,\partial\beta_{st}$.

The mutual atom polarizability $\pi_{rr,ss}$ and the bond-atom polarizability $\pi_{st,rr}$ can be obtained as simple expressions involving the orbital coefficients. Coulson & Longuet-Higgins (1947) give the following relationships

$$\pi_{rr,ss} = 2\sum_{J=1}^{M}\sum_{k=M+1}^{N}\frac{c_{rJ}^2\,c_{sK}^2 + c_{rK}^2\,c_{sK}^2}{E_J - E_K} \tag{33}$$

$$\pi_{st,rr} = 2\sum_{J=1}^{M}\sum_{K=M+1}^{N}\frac{c_{rJ}\,c_{rK}(c_{sJ}\,c_{tK} + c_{tJ}\,c_{sK})}{E_J - E_K} \tag{34}$$

Equations (30), (31) and (32) are obtained through expansions in Taylor series of the appropriate quantities. Coulson and Longuet-Higgins point out that the bond-atom polarizabilities vanish for alternant hydrocarbons. We are therefore led to the conclusion that perturbation of a diagonal element h_{rr}, which is equivalent to substitution, has no effect on the bond orders but only on the atom charges.

B. Perturbation $\delta\beta_{sr}$ in the Element h_{rs}

The change in energy which arises due to a change in the off-diagonal element h_{rs} may be expressed as a Taylor series

$$\delta E = \frac{\partial E}{\partial \beta_{rs}}\delta\beta_{rs} + \frac{1}{2}\frac{\partial^2 E}{\partial \beta_{rs}^2}\delta\beta_{rs}^2 \tag{35}$$

Using equation (26) this becomes

$$\delta E = 2P_{rs}\,\delta\beta_{rs} + \pi_{rs,rs}\,\delta\beta_{rs}^2 \tag{36}$$

$\pi_{rs,rs}$ is known as the bond self-polarizability. Coulson and Longuet-

Higgins again express the bond polarizabilities in terms of the orbital coefficients. $\pi_{rs,rs}$ is given by

$$\pi_{rs,rs} = 2 \sum_{J=1}^{M} \sum_{K=M+1}^{N} \frac{(c_{rJ}\,c_{sK} + c_{rJ}\,c_{rK})^2}{E_J - E_K} \tag{37}$$

The effect of $\delta\beta_{rs}$ on bond t—u is given by

$$\delta P_{tu} = \frac{\partial P_{tu}}{\partial \beta_{rs}} \delta\beta_{rs} = \pi_{tu,rs}\,\delta\beta_{rs} \tag{38}$$

where $\pi_{tu,rs}$ is the mutual bond polarizability which is given by

$$\pi_{tu,rs} = 2 \sum_{J=1}^{M} \sum_{K=M+1}^{N} \frac{(c_{rJ}\,c_{sK} + c_{sJ}\,c_{rK})\,(c_{tJ}\,c_{uK} + c_{uJ}\,c_{tK})}{E_J - E_K} \tag{39}$$

The effect of $\delta\beta_{rs}$ on P_{mm} is given by

$$\delta P_{mm} = \pi_{mm,rs}\,\delta\beta_{rs} \tag{40}$$

where $\pi_{mm,rs}$ is the atom-bond polarizability $(= \frac{1}{2}\pi_{rs,mm})$. Again these quantities vanish for alternant hydrocarbons, which means that to this degree of approximation perturbations in bonds have no effects on the atom charge densities.

C. Combined Effects of Several Perturbations

The energy change due to a set of diagonal perturbations $\sum_r \delta\alpha_r$ and a set of bond perturbations $\sum_{st} \delta\beta_{st}$ is given by

$$\delta E - \sum_{r,o} (\tfrac{1}{2}\pi_{rr,rr}\,\delta\alpha_r + \tfrac{1}{2}\pi_{oo,rr}\,\delta\alpha_r^2) + \sum_{st} (2P_{st}\,\delta\beta_{rs} + \pi_{st,st}\,\delta\beta_{st}^2) \tag{41}$$

The change in an atom charge δP_{rr} is given by

$$\delta P_{rr} = \sum_{s} \pi_{rr,ss}\,\delta\alpha_s + \sum_{st} \pi_{rr,st}\,\delta\beta_{st} \tag{42}$$

and the change in a bond order P_{rs} is given by

$$\delta P_{rs} = \sum_{t} \pi_{rs,tt}\,\delta\alpha_t + \sum_{tu} \pi_{rs,tu}\,\delta\beta_{tu} \tag{43}$$

The results given by this theory are in good agreement with those obtained by direct solution of the secular determinant provided that the perturbations are small (see Fig. 25).

6. The Steepest Descents Method

In most cases it is unnecessary to know the individual MO coefficients; it is only necessary to know the charges and bond orders. McWeeny (1956a,b) has shown that it is possible to calculate these quantities directly without knowledge of the explicit form of the MOs. Writing the charge and bond order matrix $\mathbf{P} = 2\mathbf{T}\,\mathbf{T}^{\dagger} = 2\mathbf{R}$ (where $\mathbf{T}$ is the matrix having as columns the coefficients of the $N/2$ occupied molecular orbitals), $\mathbf{R}$ is first guessed and then systematically corrected by a matrix method.

We shall not go into the mathematics of the method here, but it is based on obtaining a matrix of residuals which define the direction of "steepest descent" on the many-dimensional energy surface. The length of the step is then determined, from which an improved $\mathbf{R}$ can be obtained. The process is repeated until the energy minimum is reached. We shall give only the mechanics of applying the method here, for a detailed analysis McWeeny's original papers should be consulted.

The one condition on $\mathbf{R}$ is that it is kept idempotent, i.e. $\mathbf{R}^2 = \mathbf{R}$, in order to satisfy the orthonormality conditions, for if $\mathbf{T}^{\dagger}\mathbf{T} = \mathbf{z}$ then $\mathbf{R}$ may be factored into $\mathbf{T}\mathbf{T}^{\dagger}$ (but a non-idempotent matrix may be made so by a simple iterative method, if $\mathbf{R}$ is not idempotent then evaluate $\mathbf{R}_1 = \mathbf{R}^2(3.\mathbf{1} - 2\mathbf{R})$ and then iterate until $\mathbf{R}$ is idempotent).

The steps in the iterative method are (starting with an idempotent $\mathbf{R}_0$) are

1. form $\mathbf{s} = (\mathbf{1} - \mathbf{R}_0)\mathbf{h}\mathbf{R}_0$;
2. write $\mathbf{L} = \mathbf{s} + \mathbf{s}^{\dagger}$ and $\mathbf{M} = \mathbf{s} - \mathbf{s}^{\dagger}$ and compute $\mathbf{LM}$;
3. evaluate $\lambda = / -\mathrm{tr}\,\mathbf{Lh}/2\,\mathrm{tr}\,\mathbf{LMh}$;
4. make the correction $\delta\mathbf{R} = -\lambda\mathbf{L} - \lambda^2\mathbf{LM}$.

Calling the corrected matrix $\mathbf{R}_1$, repetition leads to a sequence $\mathbf{R}_0, \mathbf{R}_1 \ldots \mathbf{R}_n$ which converges rapidly to the exact value. The method is based upon a "steepest descent" process (see Cauchy, 1847; Temple, 1939).

Idempotency is not exactly preserved because the theory as it is given above includes first- and second-order changes only. Idempotency can be easily restored using the process given above.

The total π-electron energy of a system is given in the Hückel approximation by

$$E = 2\sum_J E_J = 2\sum_J^{\text{occ}}\sum_{rs} c_{rJ}\,h_{rs}\,c_{sJ} = 2\sum_{r,s} R_{sr}\,h_{rs} = 2\,\mathrm{tr}\,\mathbf{Rh} \tag{44}$$

If our starting density matrix $\mathbf{R}_0$ is the exact solution for a pure hydrocarbon, we can obtain the solution for a heterocyclic derivative very easily. In the heterocyclic one or more of the diagonal elements of the Hamiltonian change from α to $\alpha + \delta.\beta$ say, and the Hamiltonian matrix may then be represented by $\mathbf{h}_0 + \boldsymbol{\delta}\mathbf{h}$. Then we have

$$\begin{aligned} \mathbf{s} &= (\mathbf{1} - \mathbf{R})\,(\mathbf{h}_0 + \delta\mathbf{h})\,\mathbf{R}_0 \\ &= (\mathbf{1} - \mathbf{R}_0)\,\mathbf{h}_0\,\mathbf{R}_0 + (\mathbf{1} - \mathbf{R}_0)\,\delta\mathbf{h}\mathbf{R}_0 \\ &= (\mathbf{1} - \mathbf{R}_0)\,\delta\mathbf{h}\mathbf{R}_0 \end{aligned} \tag{45}$$

the first term vanishing because if $\mathbf{R}_0 = \mathbf{T}_0\mathbf{T}_0^\dagger$ is exact then the term $(\mathbf{1}-\mathbf{R}_0)\mathbf{h}_0\mathbf{R}_0$ becomes

$$\begin{aligned}\mathbf{h}_0\mathbf{R}_0-\mathbf{R}_0\mathbf{h}_0\mathbf{R}_0 &= \mathbf{h}_0\mathbf{T}_0\mathbf{T}_0^\dagger-\mathbf{T}_0\mathbf{T}_0^\dagger\mathbf{h}_0\mathbf{T}_0\mathbf{T}_0^\dagger \\ &= (\mathbf{h}_0\mathbf{T}_0-\mathbf{T}_0\mathbf{E}_0)\mathbf{T}_0^\dagger \end{aligned} \tag{46}$$

which disappears because $\mathbf{T}_0$ is the matrix of some of the eigenvectors of $\mathbf{h}_0$.

7. Perturbation Theory in the Density Matrix Method

Consider a single diagonal perturbation Δ in the element h_{ii}. From (45) the elements of $\mathbf{s}$ can be written down. $\mathbf{L}$ and $\mathbf{M}$ may then be written down by inspection and $\mathbf{LM}$ formed in the usual way. The elements of $\mathbf{L}$ and $\mathbf{LM}$ are found to have the following forms (McWeeny, 1956b),

$$\left.\begin{aligned} L_{rs} &= \Delta(R'_{rs}R_{is}+R_{ri}R'_{is}) \\ LM_{rs} &= \Delta^2(R'_{ii}R_{ri}R_{is}-R_{ii}R'_{ri}R'_{is}) \end{aligned}\right\} \tag{47}$$

where $\mathbf{R}' = (\mathbf{1}-\mathbf{R})$.

For an alternant where $R_{ii} = \frac{1}{2}$, LM_{rs} becomes

$$LM_{rs} = \tfrac{1}{2}\Delta(R_{ri}R_{is}-R'_{is}R'_{ri}) \tag{47'}$$

The step length λ is given by $-a/2b$ where $a = \operatorname{tr} Lh$ and $b = \operatorname{tr} LMh$. a and b have the values

$$\left.\begin{aligned} a &= 2\Delta^2 R_{ii}(1-R_{ii}) \\ b &= \Delta^2 \sum_j R_{ij} - \Delta^3(2R_{ii}^3-3R_{ii}^2+R_{ii}) \end{aligned}\right\} \tag{48}$$

where the summation j is carried out over all nearest neighbours of i. It is assumed that the elements of the Hamiltonian are expressed in units of β throughout.

If the molecule is an alternant then (48) simplifies further, giving

$$\begin{aligned} a &= \tfrac{1}{2}\Delta^2 \\ b &= \sum_j R_{ij}\Delta^2 \end{aligned} \quad \text{and} \quad \lambda = \frac{1}{2\sum_j R_{ij}} \tag{49}$$

The corrected R can then be written

$$R_1 = R-\lambda L-\lambda^2 LM \tag{50}$$

This matrix will be idempotent if the perturbation is not large, and if it is not so then idempotency can be restored if required by means of the technique given above.

It is possible to extend this result to the case where two diagonal elements have been perturbed, i.e. for disubstitution in a conjugated molecule. This has been investigated for the case of the unperturbed molecule being an alternant (Peacock, 1958). If we assume both heterocyclic atoms (i and j say) to be the same, as before adopt α for a carbon atom as energy zero and β as the energy unit, then the perturbation matrix has two diagonal elements. The elements of **L** and **LM** may readily be found (assuming **R** to be real) and are

$$L_{rs} = -2\Delta(R_{ri}R_{is}+R_{rj}R_{js}) \qquad LM_{rs} = -2\Delta^2(R_{is}R_{rj}+R_{js}R_{ri})R_{ij}$$
$$L_{rr} = -2\Delta(R_{ri}^2+R_{rj}^2) \qquad LM_{rr} = 0$$
$$L_{ri} = -2\Delta R_{rj}R_{ij} \qquad LM_{ri} = \Delta^2(\tfrac{1}{2}R_{ri}-2R_{ji}^2R_{ri})$$
$$L_{ii} = L_{jj} = \tfrac{1}{2}\Delta(1-4R_{ij}^2) \qquad LM_{ii} = LM_{jj}$$
$$L_{ij} = 0 \qquad LM_{ij} = LM_{ji} = \Delta^2R_{ij}(\tfrac{1}{2}-2R_{ij}^2)$$

Then

$$\mathrm{tr}\,\mathbf{Lh} = \Delta^2(1-4R_{ij}^2)$$

and

$$\mathrm{tr}\,(\mathbf{LM})\,\mathbf{h} = 2\Delta^2\sum LM_{rs} \quad \left(\sum_{rs} \text{ being a sum over real bonds}\right)$$

λ may be approximated by

$$\lambda = \frac{-(1-4R_{ij}^2)}{4\sum\limits_{rs} LM_{rs}}$$

however, if Δ is large ($>0{\cdot}75$) we must use a higher approximation for λ (see McWeeny, 1956b, p. 362), in which λ is given by

$$3(0{\cdot}25-2R_{ij}^2+4R_{ij}^4)\,\Delta\lambda^2-4\lambda\sum_{rs}LM_{rs}-(1-4R_{ij}^2) = 0$$

The corrected density matrix $\mathbf{R}_1$ is then

$$\mathbf{R}_1 = \mathbf{R}_0-\lambda\mathrm{N}-\lambda^2\mathbf{LM}$$

This matrix will be idempotent, unless Δ is large in which case it can be made so by iteration, and most of the correction is achieved here in what is the first cycle of the density matrix procedure. Subsequent iterations would, of course, be made using the full Hamiltonian as discussed in Section 7.

8. Comparison of the Perturbation Methods

The two perturbation methods discussed in Sections 6 and 8 have been used to investigate the effect of the nature and position of substituents for all cases of two equal substitutions in a benzene ring. In the case of nitrogen substitution this gives the series known as the diazines, i.e. pyridazine, pyrimidine and pyrazine when the nitrogens are *ortho*, *meta* and *para* to each other. The values of Δ used range from 0·5 to 2·0. The effects of size and position of the substituents on the energies, charge densities and bond orders are shown in Fig. 25(*b*), together with the effects of one substituent (which in the case of nitrogen substitution yields pyridine). The numbering of the atoms is given in Fig. 25*a*.

In Fig. 25(*b*) we compare these results obtained by direct solution of the secular determinant with those obtained by the steepest descents perturbation theory and with those obtained using the Coulson and Longuet-Higgins perturbation theory.

The first conclusion to be drawn from the graphs concerns the accuracy which can be obtained using the steepest descents perturbation method. The only significant discrepancies are in the bond orders at higher values of Δ. For low values of Δ the results are almost identical with those obtained from exact solution of the secular determinant; and over the whole range there is a significant improvement using "steepest descents" over the standard (Coulson and Longuet-Higgins) perturbation theory. In particular it should be noted that:

1. *Energy.* The energy in all cases appears to vary almost linearly with Δ.

2. *Charges.* The charges on the atoms show initially an almost linear variation with Δ but with values greater than unity the variation is no longer linear (the superiority of the steepest descents over the conventional perturbation method). Table 13 gives the values of the charge distribution in all four cases for the four values of Δ used obtained by direct solution of the secular determinant.

TABLE 13. Charges and bond orders for substituted benzene

	Monosubstituted benzene				*o*-Disubstituted benzene		
Δ	P_{11}	P_{22}	P_{33}	P_{44}	P_{11}	P_{22}	P_{33}
0·5	1·194	0·922	1·004	0·950	1·122	0·922	0·954
1·0	1·370	0·854	1·008	0·902	1·264	0·830	0·906
1·5	1·512	0·800	1·010	0·866	1·422	0·720	0·860
2·0	1·622	0·760	1·012	0·834	1·572	0·604	0·822

	m-Disubstituted benzene				*p*-Disubstituted benzene	
Δ	P_{11}	P_{22}	P_{44}	P_{55}	P_{11}	P_{22}
0·5	1·198	0·844	0·874	1·010	1·148	0·926
1·0	1·374	0·700	0·768	1·018	1·288	0·856
1·5	1·516	0·572	0·688	1·024	1·418	0·792
2·0	1·618	0·464	0·634	1·030	1·530	0·734

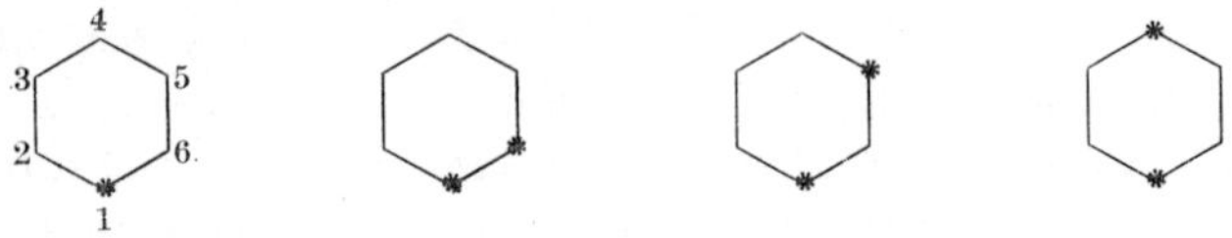

(a)

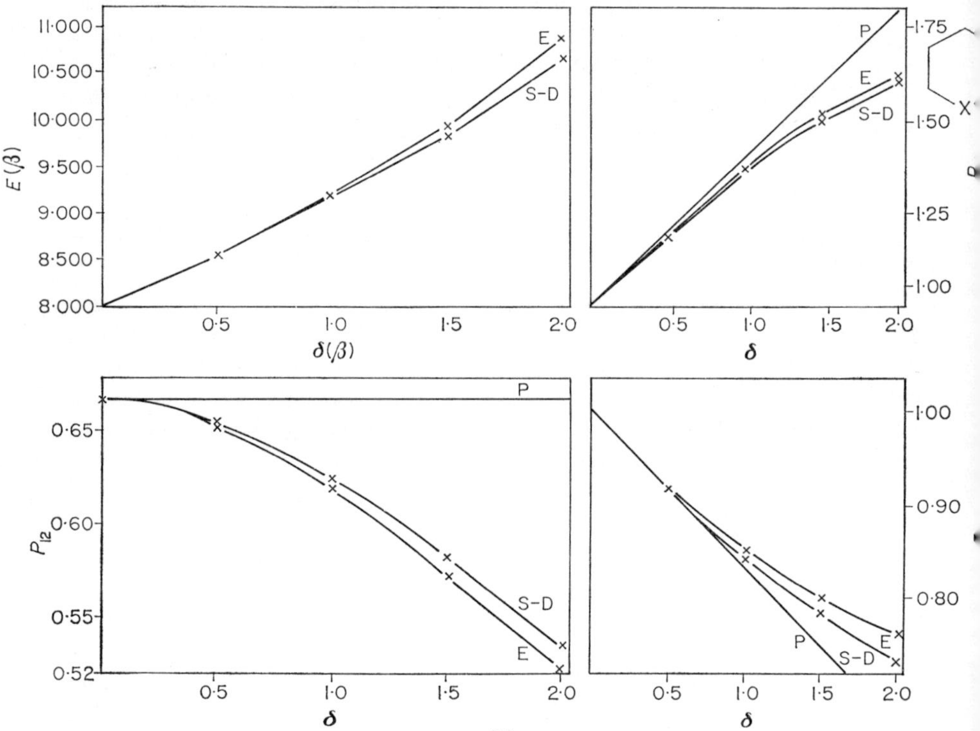

(b)

FIG. 25. (a), (b).

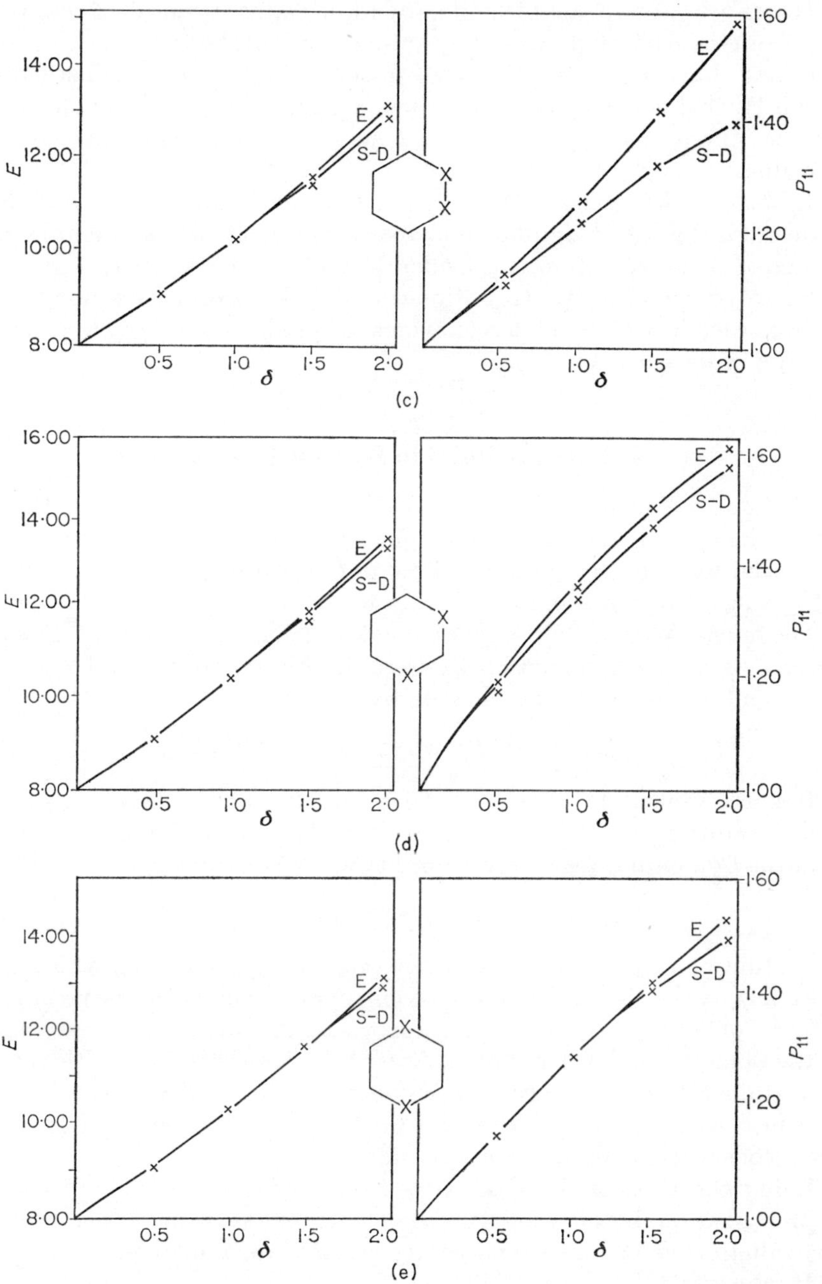

FIG. 25 continued. (c)–(e). Effects of size and of position of substituent on energy, charge density and bond order. E, exact solution of secular determinant; S–D, steepest descent approximation method; p, Coulson–Longuet-Higgins polarizability method.

The effects of two substituents are additive for values of Δ less than one, from the pattern produced by one substituent, but when Δ is greater than one this is no longer the case. In the case of nitrogen substitution where Hückel calculations have taken a value about 0·5, the effects of the two nitrogens are additive and may be estimated from those in pyridine.

3. *Bond Orders*. These are only affected in second order. At small values of Δ there is no significant change in the bond orders; but at higher values of Δ the variation is considerable. This indicates once again the failure of conventional perturbation where the bond orders are unaffected in first order. The steepest descents method predicts the correct variation of bond order with Δ.

9. Polarizabilities in Steepest Descents

The mutual polarizability of two atoms π_{ij}, is defined (following Coulson and Longuet-Higgins) as the change in charge density of atom i induced by unit change in the Coulomb integral of atom j. $\pi_{i,i}$ is the self-polarizability of atom i.

The mutual polarizability of two bonds is defined as the change in bond order r—s per unit change in the resonance integral of bond i—j, the effect on the bond order P_{rs} is given by

$$\delta P_{rs} = \pi_{rs,ij}\,\Delta_{ij} \tag{51}$$

It is convenient to adopt the same double suffix notation for atom polarizabilities. The change in charge density of atom j due to a change Δ in the Coulomb integral for atom i is then given by

$$\delta P_{jj} = \pi_{ii,ii}\,\Delta_{ii} \tag{52}$$

The atom-bond polarizabilities then become $\pi_{ii,rs}$ and $\pi_{rs,ii}$ which give the effect on the charge density of atom i per unit change in the resonance integral of bond r—s, and the effect on the bond order r—s of unit change in the Coulomb integral of atom i. As we have seen these quantities are of great importance, not only in discussing the effects of substituents but also in theories of reactivities and in the interpretation of vibrational force constants as discussed in Chapter 3.

Using the Coulson–Longuet-Higgins theory the polarizabilities are expressed as double sums of MO coefficients, but these are in fact tedious to evaluate, even when the necessary orbitals are available.

It is possible, however, to obtain much simpler approximate polarizabilities by the density matrix theory (i.e. directly in terms of the elements of P).

McWeeny (1956b) has defined the following basic quantities

$$\pi_i = \frac{1}{2v_i} \qquad (v_i \text{ sum of the orders of real bonds about } i)$$

$$\pi_{ij} = \frac{(1-P_{ij})^2}{v_{ij}} \qquad (v_{ij} \text{ sum of the orders of real bonds about } i \text{ and } j \text{ omitting } P_{ij})$$

The polarizabilities may then be approximated by

$$\left.\begin{aligned}
\pi_{ii,ii} &= \pi_i & \pi_{ij,ij} &= (1-P_{ij}^2)\pi_{ij} \\
\pi_{is,ii} &= 0 (s \neq i) & \pi_{ij,ri} &= -P_{ij}P_{ri}\pi_{ri}(r \neq i,j) \\
\pi_{rs,ii} &= -P_{ri}P_{is}\pi_i & \pi_{ij,rs} &= -(P_{ri}P_{js}+P_{rj}P_{is})\pi_{rs} \\
\pi_{rr,ii} &= -P_{ri}^2\pi_i & \pi_{ii,rs} &= \pi_{ii,rs} = 0(r \neq s)
\end{aligned}\right\} \quad (53)$$

These quantities are very easy to compute and it will be shown that they may be taken over into self-consistent field theory with only slight modification.

It is interesting to compare the "steepest descents" polarizabilities with those calculated by the Coulson and Longuet-Higgins method. In Table 14 the polarizabilities are given for benzene in the two methods.

TABLE 14. Comparison of polarizabilities in the two methods

	Steepest descents		Coulson and Longuet-Higgins		
Benzene	r	1	r	1	
	s		s	0·398	
	1	0·375	1		$\pi_{rr,ss} \times \beta$
	2	−0·167	2	−0·157	
	3	0·000	3	0·009	
	4	−0·042	4	−0·102	
	rs	1–2	rs	1–2	
	tu		tu		
	1–2	0·232	1–2	0·241	
	2–3	−0·186	2–3	−0·204	$\pi_{rs,tu} \times \beta$
	3–4	0·093	3–4	0·130	
	4–5	−0·046	4–5	−0·093	

It can be seen that there is good agreement between the two methods.

References

Cauchy, A. L. (1847). *C. r. hebd. Séanc. Acad. Sci., Paris*, **25**, 536.
Coulson, C. A. & Longuet-Higgins, H. C. (1947). *Proc. R. Soc.* **A191**, 39; **A192**, 16.
Coulson, C. A. & Anno, T. (1961). *Proc. R. Soc.* **264**, 165.

Dewar, M. J. S. (1952). *J. Am. chem. Soc.* **74**, 3345.
Dewar, M. J. S. & Schmeising, H. N. (1959). *Tetrahedron* **5**, 166.
Lennard-Jones, J. E. (1937). *Proc. R. Soc.* **A158**, 280.
Longuet-Higgins, H. C. & Salem, L. (1959). *Proc. R. Soc.* **A251**, 172.
McWeeny, R. (1951). *J. chem. Phys.* **19**, 1614.
McWeeny, R. (1956a). *Proc. R. Soc.* **A235**, 496.
McWeeny, R. (1956b). *Proc. R. Soc.* **A237**, 355.
McWeeny, R. & Peacock, T. E. (1957). *Proc. phys. Soc.* **A70**, 41.
Mulliken, R. S. (1949). *J. Chim. phys.* **46**, 497.
Mulliken, R. S., Rieke, C. A. & Brown, W. G. (1941). *J. Am. chem. Soc.* **63**, 41.
Peacock, T. E. (1958). Ph.D. Thesis, University of Durham.
Peacock, T. E. (1959). *J. chem. Soc.* 3241.
Simonetta, M. & Winstein, S. (1954). *J. Am. chem. Soc.* **76**, 18.
Streitweiser, A., Jr. (1961). "Molecular Orbital Theory for Organic Chemists." J. Wiley and Sons Inc., New York.
Tsugi, M., Huzinaga, S. & Hasino, T. (1960). *Rev. mod. Phys.* **32**, 425.
Temple, G. (1939). *Proc. R. Soc.* **A169**, 476.
Wheland, G. W. (1941). *J. Am. chem. Soc.* **63**, 2025.
Wheland, G. W. & Mann, D. E. (1949). *J. chem. Phys.* **17**, 264.
Wheland, G. W. & Pauling, L. (1935). *J. Am. chem. Soc.* **57**, 2086.

CHAPTER 5

The Self-consistent Field Theory

It is now time to examine the self-consistent field theory of conjugate and aromatic molecules. Calculations of this type fall into two categories, those which are completely non-empirical and those in which certain integrals are regarded as parameters which are determined by appeal to experiment. There are several variants of the self-consistent field and we shall attempt to examine the more important of these.

1. The Goeppert-Mayer and Sklar Approach

Goeppert-Mayer & Sklar (1938) write the Hamiltonian for the π-electron system in the following way.

$$h + H_{\text{core}} + \tfrac{1}{2} \sum_{12} r_{12}^{-1} \tag{1}$$

In other words, the π-electrons are regarded as core electrons which can be factored out of the problem. The two-electron interactions are properly included and the core terms represent the interaction of the individual π-electrons with tightly bound σ-core.

They assume that the potential arising from the nuclei and their core electrons can be approximated by that of a carbon atom in its sp_2 valence state minus the one remaining p-electron. Making this assumption, then the core part of (1) becomes

$$H_{\text{core}} = \sum_{i} H_{\text{core}\, i} \tag{2}$$

where i runs over all of the atoms in the conjugated system.

The H_{ci} of (2) each have the form

$$H_{ci} = T_i + V_i^{+} \tag{3}$$

where T_i is the kinetic energy operator and V_r^{+} is the potential defined above. If V_i is the potential operator of a neutral atom in its valence state, then the operator for the ion in the valence state V_r^{+} is given by

$$V_r^{+} = V_r - \int \phi_r \frac{e^2}{r_{12}} \phi_r \, dv \tag{4}$$

where ϕ_r is an atomic $2p$-orbital which is involved in the formation of the π-orbitals. It then follows that

$$(T + V_i)\,\phi_r = W_i \phi_i \tag{5}$$

where W_i is the energy of the $2p$-electron in the atomic system considered, and is numerically equal to the valence state ionization potential.

The ith element of the core Hamiltonian then becomes

$$\left.\begin{aligned} H_{cii} &= W_i - \sum_{j \neq k} (V_j|ii) - \sum_{j \neq i} (ij|g|ij) \\ \text{and} \quad & \\ H_{ij} &= -\sum_k (V_k|ij) \end{aligned}\right\} \tag{6}$$

where $(V_k|ij)$ the so-called penetration integral is given by

$$(V_k|ij) = \int \phi_i(1)\, V_k(1)\, \phi_j(1)\, dv_1 \tag{7}$$

where the integration is over the space of electron 1. The $(ij|g|ij)$ are the Coulomb integrals defined in (1.9)

$$(ij|g|ij) = \int \frac{\phi_i(1)\, \phi_j^*(2)\, \phi_i(1)\, \phi_j(2)}{dv_{12}}\, dv_1\, dv_2 \tag{8}$$

but where the atomic orbitals ϕ_i and ϕ_j are $2p$-orbitals on different atoms.

The value of W_i can be estimated without undue difficulty. Goeppert-Mayer and Sklar calculated the values of the integrals occurring in (6) for benzene. The results which are obtained are far from satisfactory, which is not surprising when one considers the nature of the approximations made by them. The value of this approach in the calculation of spectra will be taken up at a later stage.

The lasting importance of the Goeppert-Mayer approach is that all subsequent π-electron self-consistent field theory has been based essentially on this approach. The main difference between later methods and the original pattern is that we no longer attempt to evaluate the core Hamiltonian but usually regard this as an empirical parameter.

2. The General Theory

The steepest descents method (McWeeny, 1956a,b) is ideally suited to finding self-consistent solutions.

The equations satisfied by the occupied self-consistent field (SCF) molecular orbitals are (see Chapter 1)

$$\left.\begin{aligned} h^F A &= \epsilon_A A \\ h^F B &= \epsilon_B B \end{aligned}\right\} \tag{9}$$

where A, B represent the molecular orbitals ψ_A, ψ_B. These may be collected into a simple matrix equation (1.50)

$$\mathbf{h}^F \mathbf{A} = \mathbf{A}\boldsymbol{\epsilon} \tag{10}$$

where $\mathbf{A} = (A, B, C\ldots)$ is the row matrix of n occupied orbitals: $\boldsymbol{\epsilon}$ is an $n \times n$ matrix whose elements are the "orbital energies" and $\mathbf{h}^F$ is the Hartree–Fock operator $\mathbf{f}+\mathbf{G}$. It is because $\mathbf{G}$ depends on the wave function and hence on the orbitals determined by (10) that iterative solution of (10) is necessary. The orbital energies and the total energy are then given by

$$\epsilon_A = (A|h|A) \tag{11}$$

$$E = \sum_A (A|h|A) = \sum_A (A|2h-G|A) = 2\sum_A \epsilon_A - \sum_A (A|G|A) \quad \text{(cf. (1.14))} \tag{12}$$

In an approximation of the LCAO type, using a set of m basis functions, $\mathbf{a} = (a, b\ldots m)$ (for example atomic orbitals), the occupied orbitals are expressed as $\mathbf{A} = \mathbf{aT}$ where $\mathbf{T}$ is an $m \times m$ matrix. Writing $\mathbf{f}$, $\mathbf{h}$ and $\mathbf{G}$ for the matrices whose elements are $f_{ab} = (a|f|b)$, $h_{ab} = (a|h|b)$ and $G_{ab} = (a|G|b)$, and using $\mathbf{R} = \mathbf{TT}^\dagger$, (10) takes the form

$$\mathbf{h}^F\mathbf{T} = \mathbf{T}\boldsymbol{\epsilon} \quad (\boldsymbol{\epsilon} \text{ diagonal}) \tag{13}$$

where $\mathbf{h}^F = \mathbf{f}+\mathbf{G}$ is an $m \times m$ matrix with elements

$$f_{ab} = (a|f|b)$$

and

$$G_{ab} = (a|G|b) = (a|2J-K|b) \tag{14}$$

Substituting for $\mathbf{J}$ and $\mathbf{K}$ from (1.11) and (1.12) and calling the coefficients of the atomic orbitals l and m in the molecular orbital A, T_{lA} and T_{mA}, (14) becomes (using (1.9) and (1.10))

$$\begin{aligned} G_{ab} &= \sum_{rs} T_{rA} T^\dagger_{As}[2(as|g|br)-(as|g|rb)] \\ &= \sum_{rs} R_{rs}[2(as|g|br)-(as|g|rb)] \end{aligned} \tag{15}$$

where $(as|g|br)$ is the two-electron integral

$$(as|g|rb) = \int \frac{a(1)\,s(2)\,r(1)\,b(2)}{r_{12}}\,dv_1\,dv_2$$

It follows that (11) and (12) become

$$\epsilon^A = (\mathbf{T}^\dagger\mathbf{hT})_{AA} \tag{16}$$

$$E = 2\,\mathrm{tr}\,\mathbf{Rh} - \mathrm{tr}\,\mathbf{RG} \tag{17}$$

These transformations would lead to an exact solution of the self-consistent field problem if the basis set of atomic orbitals was infinite and hence became a complete set; truncation of the set is, however, unavoidable and leads to the best LCAO (linear combination of atomic orbitals) approximation.

Minimization of E can be achieved by solving the secular determinant in the usual fashion or by use of the steepest descents method discussed in the last chapter. In the latter case minimization is achieved by variation of the matrix $\mathbf{R}$. If we allow $\mathbf{R}$ to change by an amount $\delta\mathbf{R}$ (subject to the retention of orthonormality $\mathbf{TT}^\dagger = \mathbf{1}$ (i.e. $\mathbf{R}^2 = \mathbf{R}$ retention of idempotency as the equivalent condition), then the change of energy will be given by

$$\delta E = 2\,\mathrm{tr}\,\boldsymbol{\delta}\mathbf{Rf} + \mathrm{tr}\,\boldsymbol{\delta}\mathbf{RG} + \mathrm{tr}\,\mathbf{R}\boldsymbol{\delta}\mathbf{G} + \mathrm{tr}\,\boldsymbol{\delta}\mathbf{R}\boldsymbol{\delta}\mathbf{G} \tag{18}$$

To first order the last term may be omitted and using the identity $\mathrm{tr}\,\mathbf{R}\boldsymbol{\delta}\mathbf{G} = \mathrm{tr}\,\boldsymbol{\delta}\mathbf{RG}$ (which follows from the definition of $\mathbf{G}$), (18) becomes

$$\delta E = 2\,\mathrm{tr}\,\boldsymbol{\delta}\mathbf{R}(\mathbf{f}+\mathbf{G}) \tag{19}$$

δE is therefore identical with the variation in $2\,\mathrm{tr}\,\mathbf{R}(\mathbf{f}+\mathbf{G})$ provided that $\mathbf{G}$ is regarded as fixed during a cycle, so that $(\mathbf{f}+\mathbf{G})$ is the Hamiltonian calculated from the original $\mathbf{R}$. δE vanishes when the columns of $\mathbf{T}$ in $\mathbf{R} = \mathbf{TT}^\dagger$ are eigenvectors of $(\mathbf{f}+\mathbf{G})$, the assumed Hamiltonian $\mathbf{h}^F$ which is ultimately self-consistent. In the conventional SCF approach this is equivalent to obtaining those orbitals which are the eigenfunctions of $\mathbf{h}^F$ and hence diagonalize the orbital energy matrix $\boldsymbol{\epsilon}$.

Now E may be minimized directly without solving the eigenvalue problem by the steepest descents method. From the last chapter, Section 7, it may be remembered that

$$\left.\begin{aligned} \mathbf{L} &= \mathbf{s}+\mathbf{s}^\dagger \\ \text{and} \qquad \mathbf{M} &= \mathbf{s}-\mathbf{s}^\dagger \end{aligned}\right\} \tag{20}$$

giving

$$\delta R = -\lambda\mathbf{L} - \lambda^2\,\mathbf{LM}$$

where λ is the approximate size of the step necessary to reach a stationary point on the energy surface.

Substituting (20) into (17) and retaining the last term in order to take into account the variation in G

$$\delta E = -2\lambda\,\mathrm{tr}\,\mathbf{Lh} - 2\lambda^2\,\mathrm{tr}\,\mathbf{LMh} + \mathrm{tr}\,(-\lambda\mathbf{L} - \lambda^2\,\mathbf{LM})\,\delta\mathbf{G} \tag{21}$$

We define a matrix $\mathbf{L}'$ (the first-order correction in $\mathbf{G}$ due to a change $\mathbf{L}$ and $\mathbf{R}$) as being formed in the same way from $\mathbf{L}$ as $\mathbf{G}$ is from $\mathbf{R}$ and introduce $a = \mathrm{tr}\,\mathbf{Lh}$, $b = \mathrm{tr}\mathbf{LMh}$ and $c = \mathrm{tr}\,\mathbf{LL}'$ then

$$\delta E = -2\lambda a - 2\lambda^2 b + \lambda^2 c \tag{22}$$

The condition for a stationary point on the energy surface is the vanishing of the differential coefficient $d(\delta E)/d\lambda$, hence

$$\frac{d(\delta E)}{d\lambda} = -2a-4\lambda b+2\lambda c = 0 \tag{23}$$

$$\lambda = -a/(2b-c)$$

$\mathbf{R}_1$ may now be written down $(\mathbf{R}_0+\mathbf{R})$ and used to compute a new $\mathbf{G}$, the process being repeated until E converges.

The inclusion of $\lambda^2 c$ in (22) gives the density matrix or steepest descents method a much superior convergence over the usual SCF process. If this term is not included then the convergence is bad, perhaps requiring as many as fifteen cycles to achieve a two-figure consistency in **R** and **G**. Inclusion of it reduces the labour to three or four cycles to obtain an **R** self-consistent to three or four figures. McWeeny (1956a) discusses the bad convergence of the usual diagonalization procedure at length. This method of calculating self-consistent fields has been used extensively by the present author in a long series of studies on the structure of aromatic hydrocarbons, their heterocyclic derivatives and other derivatives formed by substitution of a conjugated group for hydrogen.

3. π-Electron Molecules

In π-electron molecules we have used the LCAO approximation for the molecular orbitals; viz.

$$\psi_A = \sum_n c_{nA}\,\phi_n$$

Substitution of this in (14) and (15) gives

$$h^F_{rs} = (f+G)_{rs} = f_{rs}+(\sum_{tu} 2R_{tu}\{(rt|g|su)-\tfrac{1}{2}(rt|g|us)\} \tag{24}$$

If $r = s$ and $t = u$, the first two-electron integral in (24) is a "Coulomb" integral and the second an exchange integral. Now if we choose our basis AOs to be suitable orthonormal combinations of $2p$ atomic orbitals (Löwdin, 1950), it turns out that all integrals other than Coulomb integrals may be ignored, having values which are negligible (McWeeny, 1955). This means

$$(rt|g|su) \approx \delta_{rs}\,\delta_{tu}(rt|g|rt) = \delta_{rs}\,\delta_{tu}\,\gamma_{rt}, \quad \text{say} \tag{25}$$

where δ_{rs} is the Kronecker delta and has the value unity if $r = s$ and zero otherwise. In all that follows γ_{ij} will be used to represent the two-electron Coulomb integral $(ij|g|ij)$.

For diagonal elements h^F_{rr}, substitution of (25) into (24) leads to

$$h^F_{rr} = f_{rr}+R_{rr}\,\gamma_{rr}+2\sum_{s\neq r} R_{ss}\,\gamma_{sr} \tag{26}$$

Now f_{rr} represents the energy (kinetic and potential) of an electron in orbital r, in the framework field. Writing the potential energy term as $V = V_1 + V_2 + \ldots$ (one part for each framework ion) we get

$$\begin{aligned} f_{rr} &= (r|-\tfrac{1}{2}\nabla^2 + V_r|r) + \sum_{s \neq r} (r|V_s|r) \\ &= \omega_r + (r|V_s|r) \\ h^F_{rr} &= \omega_r + R_{rr}\gamma_{rr} + \sum_{s \neq r} \{2R_{ss}\gamma_{rs} + \Sigma (r|V_s|r)\} \end{aligned} \tag{27}$$

ω_r is regarded as an empirical parameter which can be determined from ionization potential data or other data. In the self-consistent theory the ω which forms part of the core Hamiltonian is the basic parameter for an atom irrespective of its environment. The variation of the core quantity with environment comes through the second term $\sum_s (r|V_s|r)$. Pople (1953), who first proposed the reduction given above, approximates the sum in (27) (which is usually small) by $(2R_{ss} - Z_s)/r_{rs}$, where Z_s is the effective charge of the framework ion s (Z_s has the value $1, 2\ldots$ if atom s contributes $1, 2\ldots$ electrons to the system), and r_{rs} is the distance from r to s. Bearing in mind the essential nature of the basis orbitals a better approximation to $(r|V_s|r)$ seems to be $-Z_s\gamma_{rs}$; (27) may then be written

$$h^F_{rr} = \alpha^F_r = \omega_r + R_{rr}\gamma_{rr} = \sum_{s \neq r} (2R_{ss} - Z_s)\gamma_{rs} \tag{28}$$

The off-diagonal elements h^F_{rs} are (again putting (25) into (24))

$$h^F_{rs} = \beta_{rs} - R_{rs}\gamma_{rs} \tag{29}$$

β_{ij} is usually assumed to be negligible except for nearest neighbours. The β_{ij} are again regarded as empirical parameters.

The energy zero is conveniently chosen such that $\alpha^F_r = 0$ for an even alternant. If also h^F_{ij} (benzene) is used as the energy unit β, then the quantities α and β differ very little from their Hückel counterparts (zero for a carbon atom (by convention) and unity for a carbon–carbon bond). For an alternant $h^F_{rr} = \alpha_c = \omega_r + \frac{1}{2}\gamma^C_{rr}$ and taking this as energy zero (28) becomes

$$h^F_{rr} = \delta\omega_r + R_{rr}\gamma_{rr} - \tfrac{1}{2}\gamma^C_{rr} + \sum_{s \neq r} (2R_{ss} - Z_s)\gamma_{rs} \tag{30}$$

where $\delta\omega_r$ is the difference between ω_r and its carbon value. The theory in this form is then applicable to heterocyclics without further modification.

For a heteroatom it is useful to compare h^F_{rr} with the corresponding quantity δ (with the same units and energy zero) of Hückel theory. This must take a compromise value independent of the charge distribution;

this would be most naturally chosen so that each framework ion has its normal complement of π-electrons (one for carbon, one for nitrogen as in pyridine and two for nitrogen as in pyrrole, etc.), i.e. by putting $2R_{ss} = Z_s$. The corresponding δ would then be identified as

$$\delta = \delta\omega + \tfrac{1}{2}(Z_r - \gamma_{rr}^{\mathrm{C}}) \tag{31}$$

When self-consistency has been established, it will be found that $\delta\omega$ differs from its Hückel value δ by an amount depending on its molecular environment. Of course, it is $\delta\omega$ which has theoretical importance as a basic parameter, not δ; but it is worth examining their connexion so that Hückel solutions may be utilized as fully as possible (e.g. in determining sensible numerical values and SCF initial approximations) and for comparative reasons.

The validity of (28) and (29) is associated with the fact that a set of atomic orbitals $a, b, c \ldots$ can be found such that $(rt|g|su)$, sometimes written as (rs, tu), is very small unless $r = s$ and $t = u$. It must be remembered that these orthogonalized atomic orbitals are not atomic $2p$-orbitals but are especially chosen to be orthogonal. In particular it should be noted that these orbitals are not centrosymmetric. Orbitals of the required type have been constructed (Hall, 1954; McWeeny, 1955). It is to the evaluation of these integrals that we must now turn our attention.

4. Evaluation of Integrals

A. Construction of a Set of Orthogonalized Orbitals

There are two ways in which a given set of non-orthogonal atomic orbitals may be made orthogonal.

(i) *The Schmidt Orthogonalization*

This is a simple application of the well-known method for making a set of non-orthogonal vectors orthogonal. Take the set of AOs a, b, c ... which are non-orthogonal. Choose a as a member of the orthogonal set. Let S_{ab} be the overlap integral between atomic orbitals a and b and similarly for the other members of the set. $\bar{b}'$, the second member of the orthogonal set, will be given by

$$\bar{b} = b - S_{ab}\, a$$

$\bar{b}$ is then renormalized, and $\bar{c}$ is evaluated in the same way to be orthogonal to $\bar{a}$ and $\bar{b}$, viz.

$$\bar{c} = c - S_{ac}\, a - S_{bc}\, b$$

The process is then repeated until the complete orthogonal set is calculated. The main disadvantage of this approach is that the final result is dependent upon which member of the original set is chosen as a member of the orthogonal set. This difficulty is obviated in the second method.

(ii) *The Lowdin Cyclic Orthogonalization*

If **a** is the row matrix (**a**, **b**, **c** ...) of $2p$ atomic orbitals and $\bar{\mathbf{a}}$ is that of orthogonalized orbitals, then (Lowdin, 1951)

$$\bar{\mathbf{a}} = \mathbf{a}\mathbf{S}^{-1/2} \tag{32}$$

where $\mathbf{S}^{-1/2}$ is the inverse square root of the matrix of overlap integrals **S**. The difficulties in orthogonalizing a set of orbitals are all in constructing $\mathbf{S}^{-1/2}$. There are two ways of doing this.

If **S** can be written as $\mathbf{1}+\mathbf{x}$, where **x** is a matrix of residuals which are small, then the powers of **S** can be evaluated by a matrix power series analogous to the binomial expansion in ordinary algebra. Thus

$$\mathbf{S}^{-1/2} = \mathbf{1} - \tfrac{1}{2}\mathbf{x} + (-\tfrac{1}{2})(-\tfrac{3}{2})\mathbf{x}^2 - \ldots \tag{33}$$

This series is convergent only if the elements of **x** are no larger than about 0·5.

A second method may be employed when **S** cannot be expressed as above. First find the eigenvalues and eigenvectors of $|\mathbf{S}-\lambda| = 0$. Next form the matrix **U** whose columns are the eigenfunctions of **S**. **S** is then thrown into diagonal form by the transformation

$$\mathbf{U}^{\dagger}\mathbf{S}\mathbf{U} = \mathbf{S}_d$$

$\mathbf{S}^n$ is then found by raising each element of $\mathbf{S}_d$ to the power n. The nth power of **S** is then found by carrying through the inverse unitary transformation

$$\mathbf{U}^{\dagger}\mathbf{S}_d^n\mathbf{U} = \mathbf{S}^n$$

Using this method the inverse square root of any overlap matrix can be found.

B. Evaluation of the One-Centre Integral $(ii|g|ii)$

This integral is usually evaluated from ionization potential and electron affinity data, following Mulliken (1949).

$$(ii|g|ii) = I - A \tag{34}$$

where I is the ionization potential and A the electron affinity.

The integral can be evaluated non-empirically in a straightforward way but values so obtained are usually high by several electron volts. The reason for this is that the computed value does not take electron correlation into account. This is taken into account in a rough and ready way using Mulliken's approximation.

C. THE TWO-ELECTRON INTEGRALS $(ij|g|ij)$

The method used here follows closely that used by Pariser & Parr (1953). For nearest neighbours the Coulomb integral is regarded as an additional semi-empirical parameter. Once determined for a given type of bond, small variations in bond length can be taken into account by either allowing the integral to vary inversely with overlap or in another way, as discussed by Peacock (1960), which will be taken up in a later chapter.

For interatomic distances greater than 2·80 Å, the uniformly charged sphere approximation was used by Pariser and Parr. According to this approximation the two-centre Coulomb integral γ_{ij} is given by

$$\gamma_{ij} = \frac{-1{\cdot}503}{r_{ij}}\left[\left(1+\left\{\frac{R_{ip}-R_j}{2r_{ij}}\right\}^2\right)^{-1/2}+\left(1+\left\{\frac{R_i+R_j}{2r_{ij}}\right\}^2\right)^{-1/2}\right] \tag{35}$$

where the unit is the β defined above which has the value $-4{\cdot}79$ eV (McWeeny & Peacock, 1957). Now

$$R_i = \frac{4{\cdot}597}{Z_i}\,\text{Å}$$

where Z_i is the Slater effective charge for an electron in a $2p$ atomic orbital; The values of Z of interest here are

Z (carbon)	3·25
Z (nitrogen)	3·90
Z (oxygen)	4·55

other values of Z can be calculated easily using Slater's rules (Slater, 1930).

To return to distances less than 2·80 Å, an empirical is used. This method is in fact an extrapolation method which is based on

$$\gamma_{ij} = \tfrac{1}{2}(\gamma_{ii}+\gamma_{jj})+ar_{ij}+br_{ij}^2 \tag{36}$$

The values of a and b are determined by appeal to the results of (35) and values for the shorter distances found by application of (36).

The formulae for the integrals between $2p$-orbitals on carbon, nitrogen and oxygen based on (36) are given below.

TABLE 15

γ_{ij}^{CC}	$= -2{\cdot}198 + 0{\cdot}5480\, r - 0{\cdot}04503\, r^2$	1
γ_{ij}^{NN}	$= -2{\cdot}562 + 0{\cdot}7587\, r - 0{\cdot}07591\, r^2$	2
γ_{ij}^{CN}	$= -2{\cdot}380 + 0{\cdot}6520\, r - 0{\cdot}06002\, r^2$	3
γ_{ij}^{CO}	$= -2{\cdot}663 + 0{\cdot}8280\, r - 0{\cdot}08704\, r^2$	4
γ_{ij}^{NO}	$= -2{\cdot}812 + 0{\cdot}9334\, r - 0{\cdot}10250\, r^2$	5
γ_{ij}^{OO}	$= -3{\cdot}060 + 1{\cdot}1079\, r - 0{\cdot}12904\, r^2$	6

All integrals are in units of β. 1, 2 and 3 are taken from Pariser & Parr (1953), 4 from Sidman (1957) and 5 and 6 from Peacock & Wilkinson (1964a).

D. EVALUATION OF THE ONE-ELECTRON TERMS

The $\delta\omega$ and the β_{ij} present the greatest difficulties. These quantities are regarded as empirical parameters which are determined once and for all from experiment. The $\delta\omega$ and the β_{ij} are by definition independent of environment and once determined are transferable from one molecule to another or from one molecular environment to another.

The values of $\delta\omega$ for nitrogen contributing one and two electrons (Peacock & McWeeny, 1957; Peacock, 1959, respectively) and for oxygen contributing one π-electron (Sidman, 1957) are

$$\delta\omega_{N(1)} = 0{\cdot}35 \qquad \delta\omega_{N(2)} = 3{\cdot}00 \qquad \delta\omega_{O} = 0{\cdot}72$$

The values for the β_{ij} are as follows for double-bond distances.

$$\beta_{ij}^{C-C} = 0{\cdot}500 \quad \text{(Pariser \& Parr, 1953)}$$
$$\beta_{ij}^{C-N} = 0{\cdot}538 \quad \text{(Pariser \& Parr, 1953)}$$
$$\beta_{ij}^{N-O} = 0{\cdot}570 \quad \text{(Peacock, 1961)}$$

For triple-bond distances

$$\beta_{ij}^{C-N} = 0{\cdot}806 \quad \text{(Peacock \& Wilkinson, 1962)}$$

The double-bond standard distance is taken to be 1·39 Å and the standard triple-bond distance 1·15 Å.

The variation of β_{ij} with bond length may be taken into account, if distances are substantially different from the standard distances, using Mulliken's formula (Mulliken, 1949). This assumes that β_{ij} varies inversely with the overlap integral S_{ij}, i.e.

$$\beta'_{ij} = \frac{S'_{ij}}{S_{ij}} \beta_{ij} \tag{37}$$

Finally, for completeness, we give the values of the monocentre two-electron integrals. In β units these are found to have the values

$$\gamma_{ii}^{C} = -2{\cdot}380 \qquad \gamma_{ii}^{N} = -2{\cdot}672 \qquad \gamma_{ii}^{O} = -3{\cdot}060$$

The first two values are taken from Pariser and Parr and the last from Sidman.

The empirically determined parameters given here have all been determined from spectroscopic data. It is a test of the method to see if these parameters are transferable not only from molecule to molecule but from property to property. It will be recalled that the failure of the Hückel method was that such values were not transferable from property to property, indeed they were not even transferable from molecule to molecule in discussing the same property in many cases.

The theory outlined above must now be applied to specific examples. We do not attempt to give a complete summary of the work which has been done in this field. There are several good bibliographies which the reader should consult for references. It is our task here merely to show the results of this type of calculation on a selection of molecules.

5. The Polyacenes

The application of Hückel theory to the polyacenes was discussed at some length in Chapter 2. Indeed, throughout this book we have discussed the polyacenes in the light of the various theories and approximations which have been met.

Benzene, the first of the polyacenes, does not present any self-consistent field problem. In this case the molecular orbitals are completely determined by symmetry considerations. The only effect of the properly defined and evaluated Hamiltonian is to change the orbital energies and the total energy of the system.

In Table 16, the orbital energies of the molecular orbitals are given for the first five members of the polyacene series.

TABLE 16. Molecular orbitals for the polyacenes

Benzene		Naphthalene		Anthracene		Naphthacene		Pentacene	
C	$1{\cdot}845\beta$	*E*	$2{\cdot}004\beta$	*G*	$2{\cdot}004\beta$	*I*	$2{\cdot}092\beta$	*K*	$2{\cdot}107\beta$
B	1·178	*D*	1·604	*F*	1·823	*H*	1·932	*J*	1·966
A	1·178	*C*	1·382	*E*	1·457	*G*	1·680	*I*	1·814
A′	−1·178	*B*	1·137	*D*	1·456	*F*	1·492	*G*	1·512
B′	−1·178	*A*	0·922	*C*	1·185	*E*	1·361	*F*	1·389
C′	−1·845	*A′*	−0·922	*B*	1·114	*D*	1·316	*E*	1·294
		B′	−1·137	*A*	0·764	*C*	1·098	*D*	1·187
		C′	−1·382			*B*	1·032	*C*	1·086
		D′	−1·604			*A*	0·673	*B*	0·917
		E′	−2·004					*A*	0·609

In Fig. 26 the charges and bond orders are given. It should be noted that several interesting features appear. As in the Hückel theory, the bond orders between members of the same set in an alternant hydrocarbon are all zero.

The figures are taken from Peacock & Wilkinson (1964b). The orbitals are arranged in ascending energy order, the bonding orbitals being labelled *ABC*... descending order from the energy zero, and the anti-bonding orbitals *A′ B′*... in ascending energy order from the energy zero. The energy of the antibonding orbitals are not given from anthracene onwards.

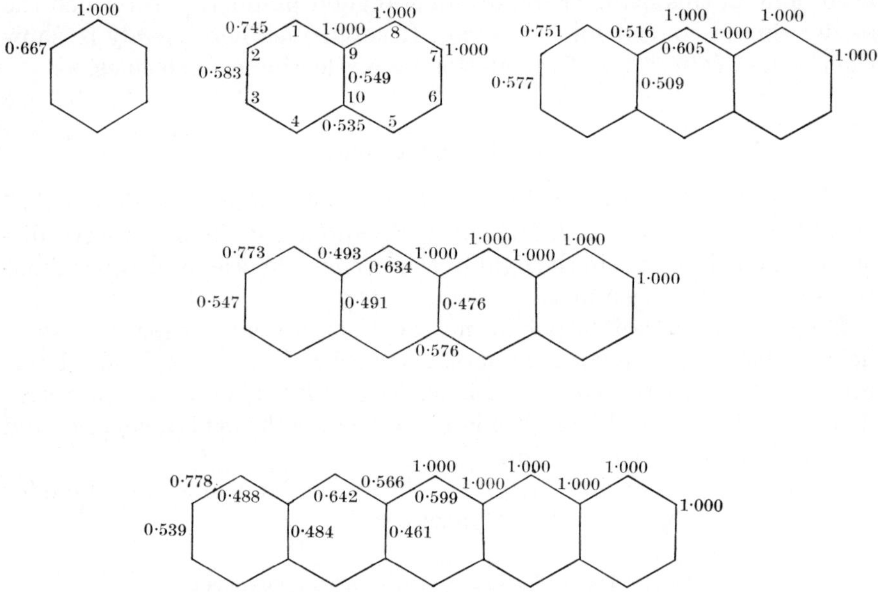

FIG. 26. Charges and bond orders for the polyacenes.

In Table 17 the orbital coefficients are given for naphthalene. Those for benzene are not given because as noted above these are completely determined by symmetry and the self-consistent problem is trivial.

From Tables 16 and 17 and from Fig. 26 several interesting conclusions may be drawn. Firstly, all of the charges are unity as in the Hückel theory, secondly, as has been pointed out, the bond orders between atoms in the same "alternant" set are all zero, whilst those between atoms in different sets are in general non-zero. This is true even for the longest "formal" bond in pentacene between atoms in different sets, here it has the value $-0{\cdot}01$.

TABLE 17. Molecular orbitals for naphthalene

$$
\begin{aligned}
E &= 0{\cdot}3031(\phi_1+\phi_4+\phi_5+\phi_8)+0{\cdot}2411(\phi_2+\phi_3+\phi_6+\phi_7)+0{\cdot}2240(\phi_9+\phi_{10})\\
D &= 0{\cdot}2636(\phi_1+\phi_4-\phi_5-\phi_8)+0{\cdot}4249(\phi_2+\phi_3-\phi_6-\phi_7)\\
C &= 0{\cdot}3984(\phi_1-\phi_4-\phi_5+\phi_8)+0{\cdot}1871(\phi_2-\phi_3-\phi_6+\phi_7)+0{\cdot}1682(\phi_9-\phi_{10})\\
B &= 0{\cdot}0040(\phi_1+\phi_4+\phi_5+\phi_8)+0{\cdot}3957(\phi_2+\phi_3+\phi_6+\phi_7)-0{\cdot}2161(\phi_9+\phi_{10})\\
A &= 0{\cdot}4249(\phi_1-\phi_4+\phi_5-\phi_8)+0{\cdot}2636(\phi_2-\phi_3+\phi_6-\phi_7)\\
A' &= 0{\cdot}4249(\phi_1+\phi_4-\phi_5-\phi_8)-0{\cdot}2636(\phi_2+\phi_3-\phi_6-\phi_7)\\
B' &= 0{\cdot}0040(\phi_1-\phi_4-\phi_5+\phi_8)-0{\cdot}3957(\phi_2-\phi_3-\phi_6+\phi_7)+0{\cdot}2161(\phi_9-\phi_{10})\\
C' &= 0{\cdot}3984(\phi_1+\phi_4+\phi_5+\phi_8)-0{\cdot}1871(\phi_2+\phi_3+\phi_6+\phi_7)-0{\cdot}1682(\phi_9+\phi_{10})\\
D' &= 0{\cdot}2636(\phi_1-\phi_4+\phi_5-\phi_8)-0{\cdot}4249(\phi_2-\phi_3+\phi_6-\phi_7)\\
E' &= 0{\cdot}3031(\phi_1-\phi_4-\phi_5+\phi_8)-0{\cdot}2411(\phi_2-\phi_3-\phi_6+\phi_7)-0{\cdot}2240(\phi_9-\phi_{10})
\end{aligned}
$$

An examination of the orbital energies for benzene and naphthalene show that the energies of bonding and antibonding orbitals are symmetrically placed about the energy zero. This is true for all of the polyacenes and is the reason why the energies of the antibonding orbitals are not given for anthracene, naphthacene and pentacene.

Examination of the orbital coefficients for naphthalene shows that the coefficients of related molecular orbitals (say X and X') are related. The coefficients of the starred or unstarred set of atomic orbitals are minus in the primed orbital what they are in the unprimed orbital, whilst those of the other set are the same in both orbitals.

From what has been noted above it can be seen that those properties of alternants which were discussed in the framework of the Hückel theory are also valid in the self-consistent field theory.

Several workers have looked at benzene, naphthalene and anthracene in the framework of self-consistent field theory, each making slight modifications to the theory. For a selection of the available calculations see, for example, Pople (1953), Kolboe & Pullman (1958), Peacock (1959), Amos & Hall (1961), and for a further study on the polyacene series, Peacock & Wilkinson (1964b).

6. Nitrogen Heterocyclics

The heterocyclic aromatic molecules present greater problems in the Hückel theory than the homocyclic hydrocarbons. It is in this sphere that self-consistent field theory has had its most rewarding results.

All hinges on the determination of the parameter $\delta\omega_{\mathrm{N}}$. It will be recalled that in the Hückel theory the corresponding δ had a value of about 0·5; this corresponds to a $\delta\omega$ value of about $0{\cdot}65\beta$. The self-consistent $\delta\omega_{\mathrm{N}}$ value used here has been determined for pyridine by fitting the calculated excited state energies with the O—O values for the observed ultra-violet bands for a series of values for the parameter. Once the best value was determined this has been used for all calculations on molecules in which nitrogen occurs in this sp_2 valence state and contributing one π-electron to the conjugated system. The best value for $\delta\omega_N$ was found to be 0·35 (McWeeny & Peacock, 1957). The corresponding δ in the Hückel theory is found to be (from (31))

$$\delta = 0{\cdot}35+\tfrac{1}{2}(-1\times 2{\cdot}672+2{\cdot}38)$$
$$= 0{\cdot}35-0{\cdot}15 = 0{\cdot}20$$

This value is much smaller than any used previously in Hückel theory. It is not suggested that this is a final choice but it is certainly of the correct order. A whole range of values have been used from $\delta = 0{\cdot}35$ (Mataga & Nishimoto, 1957) to 0·10 (Brown & Heffernan, 1959). Our value falls midway between the two.

In what follows we shall discuss pyridine, the benzene diazines, i.e. pyridazine, pyrimidine and pyrazine, and *sym*-triazine. We shall compare the results to those of the parent hydrocarbon benzene. The numbering of the five heterocyclic molecules is shown in Fig. 27.

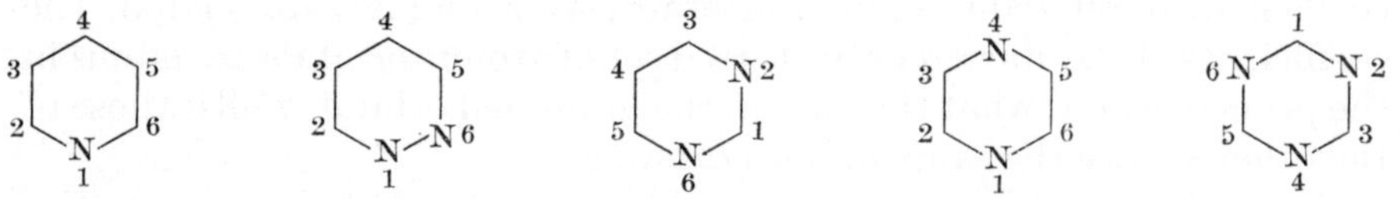

FIG. 27. Numbering of the heterocyclic molecules.

The results discussed in this section are taken from McWeeny & Peacock (1957) except where other sources are mentioned.

The elements of the self-consistent charge and bond order matrix for pyridine are given in Table 18.

TABLE 18. Charges and bond orders for pyridine

P_{11}	1·100	P_{22}	0·950	P_{25}	−0·338	P_{34}	0·670
P_{12}	0·666	P_{23}	0·662	P_{26}	−0·034	P_{35}	−0·006
P_{13}	−0·008	P_{24}	0·028	P_{33}	−1·010	P_{44}	0·980
P_{14}	−0·322						

It is interesting to compare these figures with those for benzene P_{11} 1·000, P_{12} 0·667, P_{13} 0·000 and P_{14} −0·333. Apart from the charge shifts which are of course expected, some interesting features arise from a comparison of the bond orders. The bond orders for real bonds, i.e. 1–2, 2–3 and 3–4, show very little deviation from the bond order of 0·667 for benzene. This can easily be understood when we think of some of the conclusions of perturbation theory which were discussed in the last chapter. It was noted there that the bond orders are only affected in second order, this is in accordance with the figures given in Table 18. Furthermore, small but nonetheless significant bond orders appear between atoms which in benzene are in the same "alternant" set, i.e. 1–3, 2–4 and 3–5. Finally the bond orders corresponding to long "Dewar"-type bonds which are 0·333 in benzene change by only a few units in the third figure in pyridine. In general then we can note that the bond order changes are very small, the most significant ones being in the bond orders between atomic orbitals in different "alternant" sets.

The charges and bond orders for the five heterocyclic molecules are shown in Fig. 28.

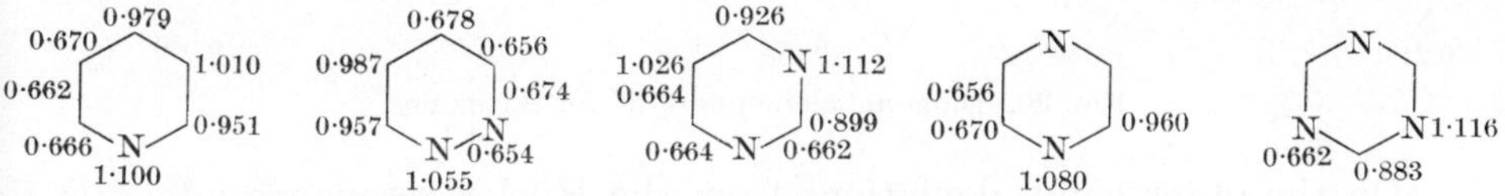

FIG. 28. Charges and bond orders for the azines.

In Fig. 29 we show the charges which result from a Hückel calculation with the corresponding δ value (i.e. 0·20).

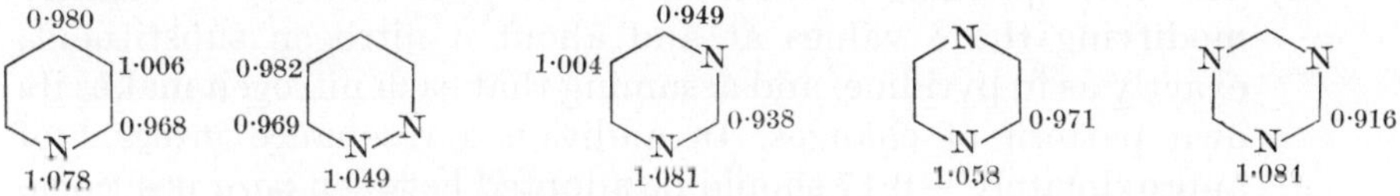

FIG. 29. Charges using Hückel method with $\delta_N = 0{\cdot}20$.

It must be stressed that these "formal" charges represent the populations of modified atomic orbitals, which are neither well-localized nor centrosymmetric, and that as they stand it would be unwise to employ them without further analysis in estimating dipole moments, etc. (see McWeeny, 1951; Peacock, 1959). For this reason we shall defer any detailed discussion of these quantities until we have discussed how they may be transformed into the corresponding quantities in a basis of ordinary $2p$ atomic orbitals. Nevertheless the elements of **P** undoubtedly have a fundamental bearing on the behaviour of the molecule besides indicating in a general way the disposition of charge. Two useful conclusions can be seen.

(i) Using the "corresponding" Hückel model with

$$\delta \approx \delta\omega_N + \tfrac{1}{2}(\gamma_{11}^N - \gamma_{11}^C),$$

the charges in Fig. 28 are reproduced to within one or two units in the second decimal place.

(ii) The shifts in the di- and tri-nitrogen heterobenzenes are almost exactly given by superimposing the effects of the separate nitrogens; so that shifts are large if the nitrogens are *meta* to each other but are diminished if they are *ortho* or (to a lesser extent) *para* to each other.

A third conclusion follows on examination of the self-consistent field Hamiltonian matrices. The diagonal elements of $\mathbf{h}^F$, the α_i^F are given in Fig. 30 and should be compared with the Hückel elements $\alpha_N = 0{\cdot}20$ (for nitrogen) and $\alpha_C = 0$ (for carbon).

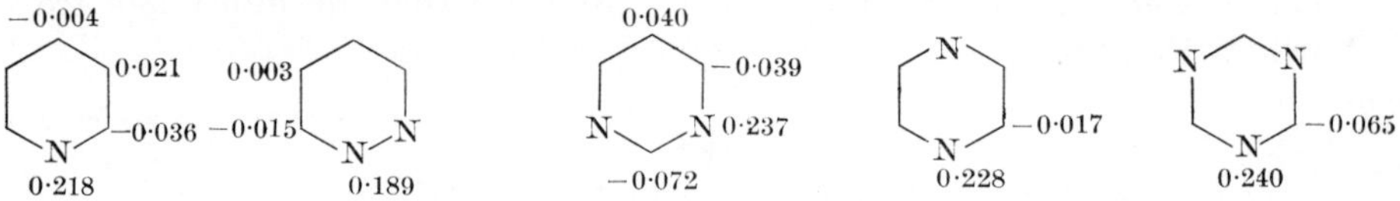

FIG. 30. Diagonal elements of $\mathbf{h}^F$ for the azines.

On the other hand, deviations from the Hückel resonance integrals (unity for a real bond, zero otherwise) are negligible, except for Dewar bonds where h_{ij}^F has values of about $-0{\cdot}17$. Moreover, the deviations introduced by different nitrogens are again roughly additive, it might in fact be said that:

(iii) The corresponding Hückel model may be refined by slightly modifying the δ values at and about a nitrogen substituent, exactly as in pyridine, and assuming that each nitrogen makes its own pattern of changes. In addition a resonance integral of approximately $-0{\cdot}17$ should be adopted between *para* positions.

From an examination of the diagonal elements of the Hamiltonian for the various azines (Fig. 30) it can be seen that positions *ortho* to the nitrogen have small negative elements. This is in contradiction to the suggestions of Pauling and Wheland who, in their "improved" Hückel model, suggested that small positive values should be given to carbon atoms adjacent to nitrogens. The self-consistent field results then provide a surprising justification for Hückel's original assumptions rather than for those of Pauling and Wheland. It seems possible that quite good approximations to true SCF results can be obtained even for more elaborate heterocyclics along these lines.

7. Substituted Benzenes

It is impossible to review here all of the work that has been done on self-consistent fields for conjugated and aromatic molecules. It is interesting, however, to look at one or two more molecules in which we have substituted groups rather than heterocyclic atoms. This provides a very severe test on the independence of the molecular parameters on environment. We shall look at the structures of benzaldehyde (McClelland, 1961), aniline (Fischer-Hjalmers, 1962) and nitrobenzene (Peacock, 1961). All of the calculations have been made using the self-consistent field method discussed above. Those other than the nitrobenzene calculation were carried out using the conventional diagonalization of the secular determinant method (following Pople, 1953). The parameters used were as follows: for benzaldehyde, $\delta = 0{\cdot}37$ for oxygen and $0{\cdot}37$ for the carbon in the carbonyl group (Sidman gives $0{\cdot}33$ and zero respectively). In the aniline calculation a $\delta\omega$ corresponding to a Hückel $\delta = 1{\cdot}0$ was used. For nitrobenzene the nitrogen parameter from the quinolizinium cation calculation (Peacock, 1959b) was used, and Sidman's parameter $\delta\omega = 0{\cdot}72$ used for the oxygen atoms.

In Fig. 31 the charges and bond orders for benzaldehyde and nitrobenzene are shown. One of the most significant features of these calculations is that there is little exchange of electrons between the group and

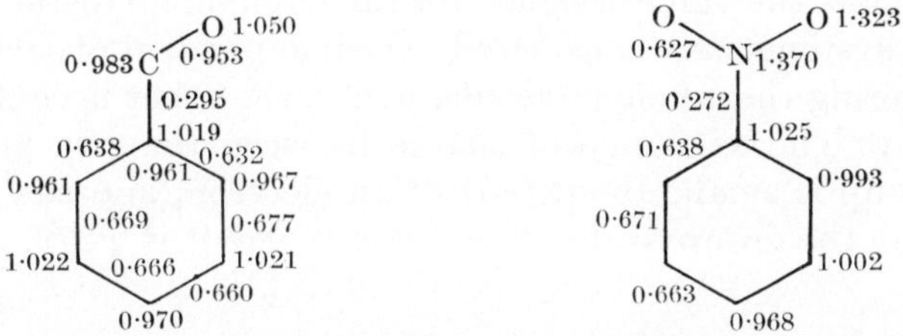

FIG. 31. Charges and bond orders for benzaldehyde and nitrobenzene.

the benzene ring. In benzaldehyde 0·05 electrons migrate from the carbonyl group into the ring, in nitrobenzene 0·016 electrons migrate from the ring into the nitro group. In the case of aniline a different state of affairs prevails. The charges and bond orders for aniline are shown in Fig. 32. It can be seen that there is a migration of some 0·065 electrons from the amino group into the ring.The greater migration in this case is due probably to the fact that there is no extra-ring conjugation beyond

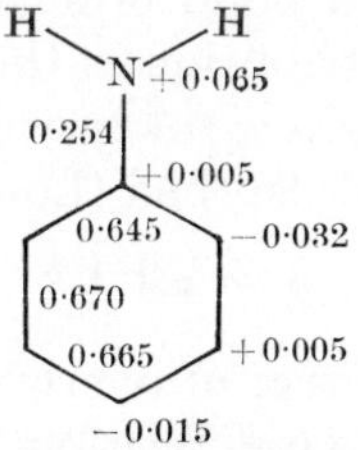

FIG. 32. Net charges and bond orders for aniline.

the one atom. We may say that in all three cases the attached group is independent of the ring, although it does exert some perturbation on the distribution of charge in the ring.

Finally in Fig. 33 we give the charges and bond orders for benzonitrile (Peacock & Wilkinson, 1962). The parameters were given the values $\delta\omega = 0{\cdot}35$ for the nitrogen and zero for the carbon atom. β_{C-N} was given

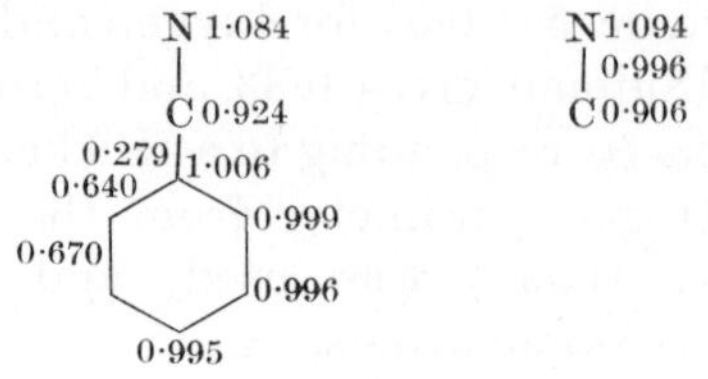

FIG. 33. Charges and bond orders for the benzonitrile molecule.

the value 0·806, the value assigned for the triple-bond distance. The two conjugated systems were considered to be independent of each other, one system covering the whole molecule, whilst the other is confined to the nitrile group. The exchange of charge between the ring and the substituent group is small, about 0·01 of an electron, and again the bond order joining the group to the ring is small, here it is 0·279.

8. The Charge and Bond Order Matrix in the Basis of Ordinary, Non-orthogonal $2p_z$-Orbitals

A density matrix process for obtaining a self-consistent field for a molecule in which the basis orbitals are non-orthogonal has been developed (McWeeny, 1959). The matrices in the two bases are, however, simply related and it is to this relation that attention is now turned.

It has been commented upon earlier in this chapter that the atomic orbitals which form an orthogonal basis are neither well-localized nor are they centrosymmetric, and therefore the $\bar{P}_{ij}$ which represent the "formal" charges $(i = j)$ and bond orders $(i \neq j)$ do not give a direct description of the charge distribution in the molecule.

If $\mathbf{a}$ is the row matrix $(a_1, a_2 \ldots a_n)$ of $2p$ atomic orbitals and $\bar{\mathbf{a}}$ that of the orthonormalized atomic orbitals, then (Lowdin, 1951).

$$\bar{\mathbf{a}} = \mathbf{a}\mathbf{S}^{-1/2} \tag{38}$$

where, as before, $\mathbf{S}$ is the matrix of overlap integrals. The $\mathbf{S}^{-1/2}$ can be calculated as discussed above (see Section 4). Let $\bar{\mathbf{T}}$ be an $m \times n$ matrix whose columns represent the coefficients of the orthogonalized atomic orbitals in the m occupied molecular orbitals. It then follows immediately that $\bar{\mathbf{A}} = (A, B\ldots) = \bar{\mathbf{a}}\bar{\mathbf{T}}$ where $\bar{\mathbf{A}}$ is the row matrix whose elements are the n occupied molecular orbitals, and the one-electron density is given by

$$P(1) = \sum_{i,j} \bar{a}_i(1)\, \bar{P}_{ij}\, a_j(1) \tag{39}$$

where $\mathbf{P} = 2\,\bar{\mathbf{T}}\mathbf{T}^{\dagger}$.

Using (38), and $\mathbf{A} = \mathbf{aT}$ where $\mathbf{T} = \mathbf{S}^{-1/2}\mathbf{T}$, the expression for $P(1)$ becomes

$$P(1) = \sum_{ij} a_i(1) P_{ij}\, a_j(1) \tag{40}$$

where $\mathbf{P} = 2\mathbf{T}\mathbf{T}^{\dagger} = \mathbf{S}^{-1/2}\mathbf{P}\mathbf{S}^{-1/2}$. $\mathbf{P}$ is then the charge and bond order matrix in the basis of ordinary $2p_z$ atomic orbitals, its elements indicating the charges in well-defined regions.

The amounts of charge localized in the orbital region (i.e. atom charge) and overlap region (bond charge) are found by integrating (40) and give

$$q_{ii} = P_{ii}$$

and

$$q_{ij} = 2P_{ij}S_{ij} \tag{41}$$

and

$$\operatorname{tr}\mathbf{PS} = N \quad \text{(the total number of electrons in the } \pi\text{-electron system)}$$

These quantities are known as orbital and overlap populations (Mulliken, 1955), or atom and bond charges (McWeeny, 1951). The definitions given here are somewhat different from those given by Mulliken.

This theory will now be applied to a study of the naphthalene molecule (Peacock, 1959a). The overlap integral between two $2p_z$ atomic orbitals is given by (Mulliken *et al.*, 1949)

$$S_{ij} = \exp(-\rho/2)\left(1+\frac{\rho}{2}+\frac{\rho^2}{10}+\frac{\rho^3}{120}\right) \tag{42}$$

where $\rho = Zr$, and Z is the effective nuclear charge on atoms i and j, and r is the interatomic distance in atomic units.

The numbering ring of the atoms was given in Fig. 5 (p. 20). The values of the overlap integrals are given in Table 19.

TABLE 19. Overlap integrals for naphthalene

S_{12}	S_{13}	S_{14}	S_{15}	S_{16}	S_{17}	S_{18}
0·260	0·039	0·002	0·000	0·000	0·001	0·018

The matrix $\mathbf{S}^{-1/2}$ can be computed as discussed above by writing S as $(\mathbf{1}+\mathbf{x})$ and expanding as a matrix power series, six terms giving adequate accuracy.

The atom and bond charges calculated using (41) are given in Table 20 and compared with that of McWeeny (1951) who set all overlap integrals between non-nearest neighbours equal to zero. The values of P_{ij} and $\bar{P}_{ij}$ are also given.

From an examination of the figures shown in Table 20 it can be seen that each atom has a deficiency of about 0·2 electrons whilst each bond contains a net negative charge of about 0·2 electrons. It can be seen that even in alternant hydrocarbons where the elements of $\bar{\mathbf{P}}$ are unity, small but significant variations of charge occur when these quantities are transformed into a corresponding quantity in the basis of ordinary atomic orbitals.

TABLE 20. Atom and bond charges in naphthalene

	11	12	22	23	33	38	1,10
q	0·759	0·300	0·772	0·177	0·737	0·211	0·200
q (McWeeny)	0·757	0·273	0·767	0·193	0·719	0·178	0·213
P	0·759	0·567	0·772	0·341	0·737	0·405	0·382
$\bar{P}$	1·000	0·754	1·000	0·526	1·000	0·576	0·572

One interesting application arises from this analysis. Using the atom and bond charges calculated using (41) and given for naphthalene in Table 20, we can calculate the potential energy contours outside of the molecule. The potential energy of a unit point charge moving in the field of the molecule may be represented by

$$V = (\delta_{rs} - q_{rs})/r_{c(rs)} \tag{43}$$

where $r_{c(rs)}$ is the distance between the point charge and the centroid of bond rs (or the atom if $r \neq s$) and q_{rs} is the atom charge or overlap charge ($r = s$ and $r \neq s$ respectively), δ_{rs} is the Kronecker delta used before, which has the value unity if $r = s$ and zero otherwise. This quantity is in fact the framework ion charge in atomic units for an atom which contributes one π-electron to the electron system. It is assumed that each framework ion may be regarded as a point positive charge. This is probably a good approximation at distances which are large enough for polarization effects to be negligible.

The potential field around naphthalene has been calculated (Peacock, 1959a) using (43). This field is shown in Fig. 34. The broken circles, of radius 5 atomic units around the centre of each ring, indicate the closest distance at which (43) may be meaningful. Of the points which lie on this circle, those opposite to bonds 1–2 and 2–3 have a potential energy twice as large as the point opposite to 1–10.

This diagram suggests the possible behaviour of a cation approaching the molecule. The cation when it enters the potential field of the molecule will be subject to strong directive influences which will tend to attract it

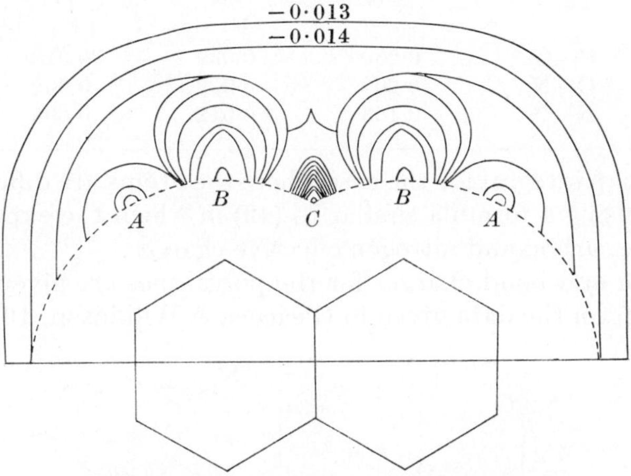

FIG. 34. Potential energy contours around the naphthalene molecule (in atomic units). (*By permission of the Chemical Society.*)

Numerical values (all negative, except as stated) of successive contours, listed outwards are:

A, 0·023, 0·021, 0·016.
B, 0·010 (positive), 0·004, 0·011, 0·013, 0·014, 0·015.
C, 0·026, 0·022, 0·021, 0·020, 0·019, 0·018, 0·017, 0·016.
At ×: *A*, 0·028; *C*, 0·028.

towards the bonds. The actual reaction between ligand and molecule will occur at distances which are so close that (43) will no longer apply. Whilst this picture is perhaps too naïve to discuss the details of the reactivity of naphthalene, it does at least lend some justification to the "π complex" theory of Dewar (Dewar, 1949). It is important, however, to notice that the usual assumptions of uniform charge distribution in conjugated hydrocarbons, where there are no net charges, lead to no directing influences on an approaching cation, whilst the simple analysis which we have given above shows that such influences are in fact there.

9. Atom and Bond Populations in the Polyacenes and Azines

Atom and bond populations have been calculated for the polyacenes (Peacock & Wilkinson, 1964b) and for the azines (Peacock, 1960). The overlap integrals for nitrogen–nitrogen orbitals is very much smaller than for carbon–carbon orbitals. The overlap integrals used in the azine calculations are given in Table 21.

TABLE 21. Overlap integrals for C—C, C—N and N—N orbitals in a six-membered ring

	S_{12}	S_{13}	S_{14}
C—C	0·260	0·039	0·018
C—N	0·200	0·022	0·009
N—N	0·153	0·012	0·005

The overlap integral for the case where the atoms are different can be calculated using a formula similar to (42) in which the exponent is the mean of the carbon and nitrogen effective charges.

The atom and bond charges for the polyacenes are given in Fig. 35, calculated from the data given in (Peacock & Wilkinson, 1964b)

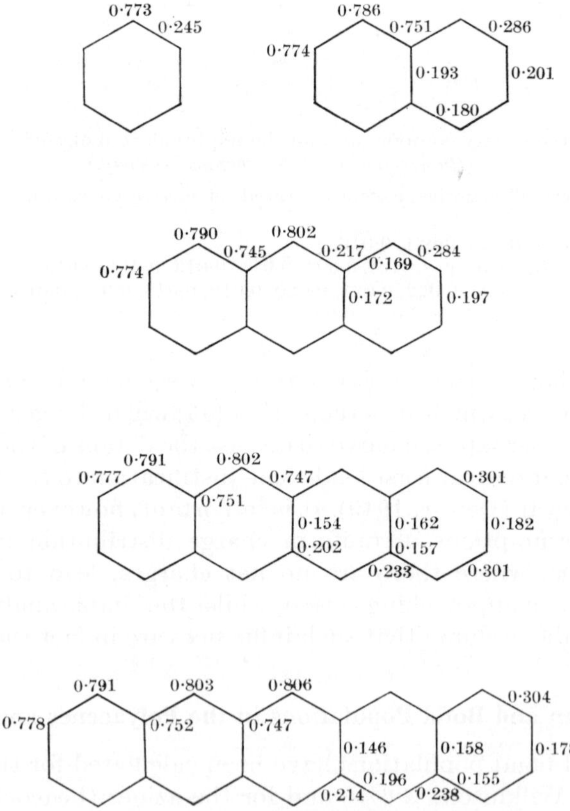

FIG. 35. Atom and bond charges in the polyacenes.

In Fig. 36 the atom and bond charges are given for the azines (taken from Peacock, 1960). It can be seen once more that there is roughly 0·2

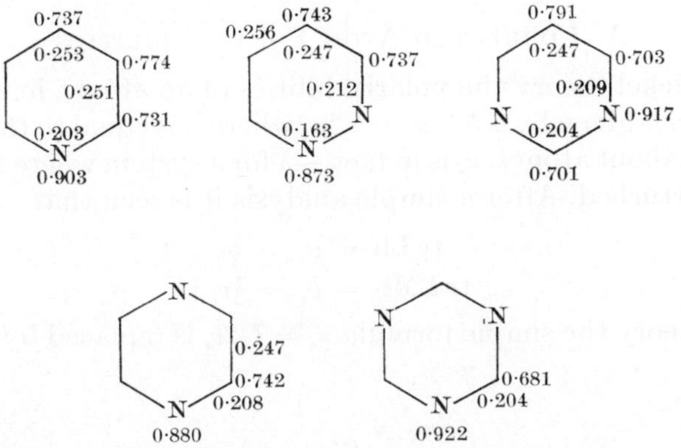

FIG. 36. Atom and bond charges in the azines.

electrons in each bond whilst the average population in an atom is about 0·8. The nitrogen atom causes the same pattern of change in the charge distribution as in the orthogonal basis.

10. Polarizabilities

In Chapter 4 the use of polarizabilities in calculating the effect of a perturbation was discussed. It was pointed out that the use of such a method is equivalent to using a first-order perturbation theory. In this chapter we shall discuss the use of polarizabilities in self-consistent field theory to calculate (*a*) a self-consistent solution for a molecule whose Hückel solution is known and (*b*) a solution for a perturbed solution when the self-consistent solution for the unperturbed problem is known.

In the first case there are several small bond perturbations, since every bond gives a contribution to the perturbation matrix (Peacock, 1957) **Δ**. The resonance integral of a bond is given by $h_{ij}^F = \beta_{ij} - R_{ij}\gamma_{ij}$ (the diagonal elements for an alternant remain zero). It was suggested by Brickstock & Pople (1954) that the Coulson and Longuet-Higgins polarizabilities could be used to obtain an SCF solution from a Hückel solution. When calculations of this type are carried through it is found that only 50% of the changes accompanying introduction of self-consistency occur. This is due to ignoring the interdependence of the Hamiltonian and the charges and bond orders, a difficulty which can be avoided by using the steepest descents method (see Section 2).

It will be recalled that in Section 9 of the last chapter, polarizabilities were defined in the basis of the steepest descents theory. It is now necessary to define certain corrected polarizabilities which take into account the interdependence of the Hamiltonian and the charge distribution.

A. Corrected Atom Polarizabilities

In the Hückel theory the polarizabilities of an atom i in an alternant hydrocarbon is given by 4·53, $\pi_i = 1/2\nu_i$ where ν_i is equal to the sum of the bond orders about atom i. π_i is in fact $-\lambda$ for a system where the ith atom has been perturbed. After a simple analysis it is seen that

$$\left.\begin{aligned} \operatorname{tr}\mathbf{Lh} &= a_i = \tfrac{1}{2} \\ \operatorname{tr}\mathbf{LMh} &= b_i = \tfrac{1}{2}\nu_i \end{aligned}\right\} \tag{44}$$

In SCF theory the simple formula $\pi_i = 1/2\nu_i$ is replaced by (McWeeny, 1956b)

$$\pi_i = \frac{1}{(2\,\nu_i - c_i)} \tag{45}$$

where ν_i is now a weighted sum of bond orders about $i(\nu_i = \sum_j P_{ij} h_{ij}$, summation over all bonds ij) and $c_i = \operatorname{tr}\mathbf{LL}'$ and corrects for the dependence of the Hamiltonian on the charge density leading to best one-descent approximation when this approximation is admitted.

$$c_i = \tfrac{1}{4}\gamma_{ii} = \tfrac{1}{4}\sum_r P_{ri}^4 \gamma_{rr} - \sum_r P_{ri}^2 \gamma_{ri} + \tfrac{1}{2}\sum_{r<s} P_{ri}^2 P_{is}^2 \gamma_{rs} \tag{46}$$

Equation (45) will be used later to calculate the SCF azine solutions using the benzene solution as a starting point.

In an alternant hydrocarbon all of the h_{ii}^F are zero and therefore there are no charge shifts accompanying the introduction of electron interaction into the Hamiltonian.

B. Corrected Bond Polarizabilities

Again using the steepest descents approach, the bond polarizabilities $\pi_{rs,ij}$ may be approximated in terms of a quantity π_{ij} which depends only on the bond orders (see Chapter 4, equation (53)). For an alternant hydrocarbon, in the simple Hückel theory, π_{ij} is given by

$$\pi_i = (1 - P_{ij}^2)/\nu_{ij} \tag{47}$$

where P_{ij} is the bond order of bond i—j and ν_{ij} is the sum of the orders of bonds about i and j omitting P_{ij}. The bond polarizabilities are then related to this quantity (see Chapter 4, equation (53))

$$\left.\begin{aligned} \pi_{ij,ij} &= (1 - P_{ij}^2)\,\pi_{ij} && \text{(a)} \\ \pi_{ij,ri} &= -P_{ij} P_{ri}\,\pi_{ri} && \text{(b)} \\ \pi_{ij,rs} &= -(P_{ri} P_{js} + P_{rj} P_{is})\,\pi_{rs} && \text{(c)} \end{aligned}\right\} \tag{48}$$

These formulae apply whether or not i—j is a real bond. Approximate preservation of self-consistency is ensured, as in the atom case, by introducing (Peacock, 1957b)

$$\pi_{ij} = \frac{(1-P_{ij}^2)}{\nu_{ij}-c_{ij}} \tag{49}$$

and continuing to use (48). ν_{ij} is now a weighted bond order sum

$$\left(= \sum_r (P_{ri}\,h_{ri} + P_{rj}\,h_{rj} - P_{ij}\,h_{ij}\right)$$

c_{ij} once again corrects for the interdependence of the Hamiltonian and charge density which is ignored in the Hückel theory. A straightforward calculation of $\operatorname{tr}\mathbf{LL}'$ gives

$$c_{ij} = \frac{1}{2}\left\{(1-P_{ij}^2)^2\gamma_{ij} + P_{ij}^2 \sum_r{}' (P_{ri}^2\gamma_{ri} + P_{rj}^2\gamma_{rj}) + \sum_{r<s}{}' (P_{ri}^2 P_{jr}^2 + P_{rj}^2 P_{is}^2)\gamma_{rs}\right\} \tag{50}$$

The primes indicate exclusion of terms where $r, s = i, j$.

C. The SCF Solution for an Alternant

For an alternant hydrocarbon the diagonal elements of $\mathbf{P}$ are unity. The Hartree–Fock Hamiltonian ($\mathbf{h}^F$) can then be estimated using the approximate density matrix of Hückel theory; for its elements are related to those of $\mathbf{P}$ by

$$\begin{aligned} h_{ii}^F &= 0 \\ h_{ij}^F &= \beta_{ij} - \tfrac{1}{2}P_{ij} \quad (i \neq j) \end{aligned} \tag{51}$$

This estimate of the self-consistent field Hamiltonian differs from the Hückel Hamiltonian, which has elements of unity for each real bond and zero otherwise, by the perturbation matrix $\mathbf{\Delta}$, which represents roughly the change necessary to produce self-consistency h^F

$$\mathbf{h}^F = \mathbf{h} + \mathbf{\Delta} \tag{52}$$

Regarding $\mathbf{\Delta}$ as a small perturbation, the effect upon the bond orders of introducing self-consistency can now be estimated in terms of (48), (49) and (50). To first order, the effects of all bond perturbations may be superimposed, giving a correction to the order of bond i—j

$$\delta P_{ij} = \sum_{r<s} \pi_{ij,rs}\,\Delta_{rs} \tag{53}$$

In order to introduce approximate self-consistency it is therefore only necessary to know the corrected mutual polarizabilities for all pairs of bonds.

D. The SCF Solution for a Heterocyclic

In going from a SCF hydrocarbon solution to the SCF heterocyclic solution, the matrix $\mathbf{\Delta}$ has a very simple form. We allow h_{ii}^F to change by an amount $\mathbf{\Delta}_{ii}$ (if atom i is substituted): this will be made up of two parts; $\delta\omega_i$ the change in the framework part, and $\delta\gamma_{ii}$ the change in the one-centre Coulomb integral. The only other elements are Δ_{ik} where i—k are the real bonds about i, and the framework β_{ij} is assumed to change by an amount $\delta\beta_{ij}$. All other elements of $\mathbf{\Delta}$ are assumed to be zero.

Considering the Δ_{ii}, the effects on the charge and bond order matrix are given by

$$\left.\begin{aligned} \delta P_{rr} &= \pi_{rr,ii}\,\Delta_{ii} = -P_{ri}^2\,\pi_i\,\Delta_{ii} \\ \delta P_{rs} &= \pi_{rs,ii}\,\Delta_{ii} = -P_{ri}P_{is}\,\pi_i\,\Delta_{ii} \end{aligned}\right\} \qquad (54)$$

where π_i is the corrected polarizability (45).

The effect of the elements Δ_{ik} are given by (48).

E. Applications to Alternant Hydrocarbons

The method outlined in Section C has been applied to the calculation of the self-consistent charge and bond order matrix for naphthalene (Peacock, 1957b). The numbering of the atoms is given below.

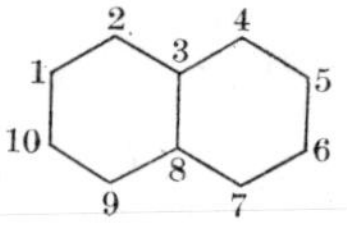

Table 22

π_{12}	π_{23}	π_{38}	$\pi_{1,10}$	$\pi_{1,8}$	π_{29}	π_{14}	π_{27}	π_{16}
0·913	0·944	0·574	1·055	0·488	0·569	0·547	0·643	0·504
Δ_{12}	Δ_{23}	Δ_{38}	$\Delta_{1,10}$	Δ_{18}	Δ_{29}	Δ_{14}	Δ_{27}	Δ_{16}
0·044	−0·084	−0·110	−0·047	−0·126	−0·189	−0·067	−0·034	+0·046

The self-consistent bond orders may now be calculated using the mutual polarizabilities and superimposition approximation. The results are compared in Table 23 with those obtained using the full iterative self-consistent process, which were given earlier, and also with the Hückel bond orders.

The values calculated using the polarizability method are seen to agree with the self-consistent values to within a few units in the third

TABLE 23

	P_{12}	P_{23}	P_{38}	$P_{1,10}$	P_{18}	P_{29}
Hückel	0·724	0·554	0·518	0·604	−0·240	−0·362
Polarizability	0·764	0·520	0·580	0·564	−0·254	−0·362
SCF	0·754	0·526	0·576	0·574	−0·252	−0·563

decimal place. Finally, if all the elements are calculated, the matrix $\mathbf{R} = \frac{1}{2}\mathbf{P}$ is almost idempotent (giving a rough check on the calculation) and can be made exactly so by iteration. This more complete result is again in excellent agreement with that obtained in the full self-consistent field calculation.

F. Application to Large Molecules

The method above, although representing a great simplification of the complete self-consistent field calculation, would at first sight become extremely tedious for large molecules. Fortunately, this is not the case owing to the rapid convergence of the sums in (50) and (53), and to the alternant character of the system, which makes many of the terms vanish. A careful examination of pyrene (Fig. 37) shows that the only significant contributions come from quite a small number of configurations of atoms i, j, r and s. Approximating the sums in this way, calculations have been extended to pyrene. The results are compared with those of the full self-consistent field calculation, and with the Hückel values in Table 24 and are seen to be in excellent agreement.

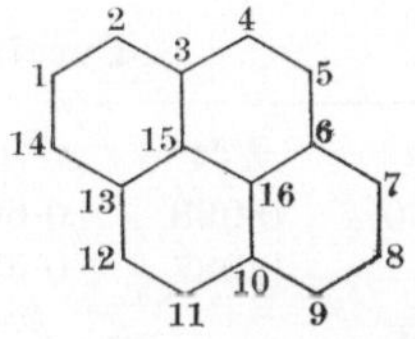

FIG. 37. The pyrene molecule.

TABLE 24

	P_{12}	P_{23}	P_{34}	$P_{3,15}$	$P_{4,15}$	$P_{15,16}$
Hückel	0·669	0·594	0·503	0·523	0·777	0·537
Polarizability	0·669	0·608	0·448	0·542	0·812	0·503
SCF	0·670	0·606	0·462	0·540	0·815	0·508

G. Application to the Azines

The calculations have also been extended to the azines. The relevant polarizabilities are

(i) Atoms

$$\pi_{11,11} = 0{\cdot}532 \quad \pi_{11,22} = -0{\cdot}236 \quad \pi_{11,44} = -0{\cdot}059$$

(ii) Bonds

$$\pi_{12,12} = 0{\cdot}433 \quad \pi_{14,14} = 0{\cdot}490$$

These polarizabilities are used to calculate the self-consistent field solutions for all of the azines, the results are given in Table 25. The numbering of the atoms is shown in Fig. 38.

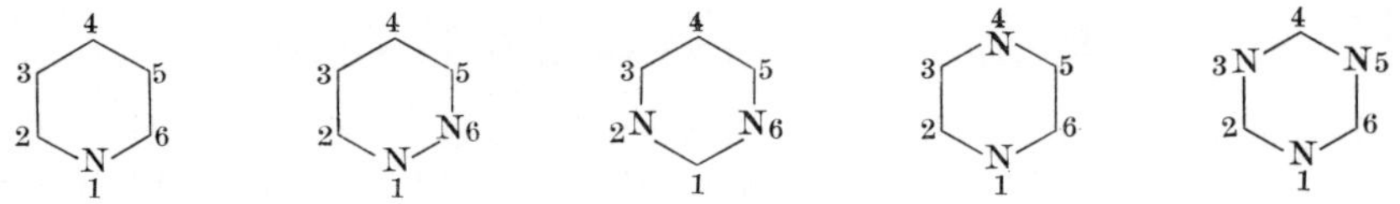

FIG. 38. The azines.

TABLE 25

	Pyridine						
	P_{11}	P_{22}	P_{33}	P_{44}	P_{12}	P_{23}	P_{34}
Benzene	1·000	1·000	1·000	1·000	0·667	0·667	0·667
Polarizability	1·113	0·950	1·000	0·988	0·668	0·660	0·670
SCF	1·100	0·951	1·010	0·979	0·666	0·662	0·668

	Pyridazine						
	P_{11}	P_{22}	P_{33}	P_{12}	P_{23}	P_{34}	P_{16}
Polarizability	1·063	0·950	0·988	0·661	0·663	0·673	0·669
SCF	1·055	0·957	0·987	0·674	0·655	0·675	0·625

	Pyrimidine						
	P_{11}	P_{22}	P_{33}	P_{44}	P_{12}	P_{23}	P_{34}
Polarizability	0·900	1·113	0·938	1·000	0·661	0·671	0·663
SCF	0·900	1·112	0·926	1·026	0·661	0·666	0·665

	Pyrazine				Triazine		
	P_{11}	P_{22}	P_{12}	P_{23}	P_{11}	P_{22}	P_{12}
Polarizability	1·101	0·950	0·671	0·653	1·113	0·888	0·663
SCF	1·080	0·960	0·670	0·656	1·116	0·883	0·664

The corrected polarizabilities enable self-consistent field charge and bond order matrices to be calculated for any alternant hydrocarbon and its heterocyclic derivatives without having to use the full matrix method. It is somewhat disappointing that the c_i and c_{ij} become tedious to evaluate as the size of the molecule increases, but it is still easy to obtain approximate self-consistent field solutions; these are sufficiently accurate for most applications and provide a satisfactory basis for refinement of the Hückel theory and its applications.

11. The Variable Electronegativity Self-consistent Field Method

Some authors have suggested that the framework parameters themselves, i.e. α–β, should be dependent on the π-charge density. This is a simple extension to the self-consistent field theory of the auxiliary inductive parameter theory of Pauling and Wheland which we have already discussed. The extension of the self-consistent field theory to take this into account has been made in a series of papers by Brown & Heffernan (see, for example, Brown & Heffernan, 1958). This modification of the theory was introduced to enable such things as dipole moments and reactivity to be discussed in the framework of the same set of parameters as is used to calculate the electronic spectrum. Hall & Amos (1960) have shown that an interpretation of π-electron dipole moments in nitrogen heterocyclics can be given without invoking such concepts, as we shall see in the next chapter. In this work we have nothing to say about the theory of the reactivity of aromatic molecules as this could itself form the subject of another volume.

In essence, the Brown and Heffernan theory allows for the variation in the electronegativity of an atom to vary with the π-electron density, P_{rr}, on that atom. This is done by regarding the effective charge Z_r as a function of P_{rr}. The relationship suggested by them is

$$Z_r = N_r - 1{\cdot}35 - 0{\cdot}35(\sigma_r + P_{rr}) \tag{54}$$

where N_r is the atomic number of atom r, and σ_r is the number of π-electrons contributed to the molecular framework by atom r, which is four for a nitrogen atom in pyridine, etc. Equation (54) follows from a direct application of Slater's rules to atoms of the first row of the periodic table.

Having admitted this dependence of Z_r on the π-electron distribution P_{rr}, all of the integrals which occur in the matrix elements of the Hamiltonian become dependent on the charge density. Brown and Heffernan, in a long series of papers, admit this dependence of the basic integrals on the charge density in a study of a large number of heterocyclic molecules.

For pyridine, Brown & Heffernan (1959) find the following values for the Hückel α-parameter in their calculations. This set of Hückel α's was found by determining that set of α's which reproduce the self-consistent field charge density rather than by the identification used above. $\alpha_N = 0{\cdot}176$, $\alpha_o = 0{\cdot}017$, $\alpha_m = 0{\cdot}003$, $\alpha_p = 0{\cdot}000$, where o, m, p refer to atoms *ortho*, *meta* and *para* to the N (this latter value is arbitrarily taken as origin). For a nitrogen atom as in pyrrole they suggest α values of about 1·5.

It is interesting that these values of α for the nitrogen atom in the different environments correspond closely to those determined independently by McWeeny & Peacock (1957) and Peacock (1959b).

The inductive parameter is found to have a very small value even for nearest neighbours. The results are not very different from those obtained by the more straightforward approach and it seems hard to justify such a technique when there are first-order problems which are still unresolved, e.g. the π-electron density and its effects on the basic parameters. We shall, however, say more of this theory in discussing the prediction of the π-electron properties of aromatic molecules in the next chapter.

12. Concluding Remarks

In this chapter we have discussed the formulation of the self-consistent field Hamiltonian and its form for the π-electron shell. One drawback to the present formulation is that this approach, even within the π-electron framework, is still incomplete. The wave function is still restricted to a single determinant. A more general wave function would be one in which the ground state is represented as a complete set of determinantal functions whose elements run over the complete set of molecular orbitals.

Such a general approach, which would result in the correct wave function, is of course impossible to follow through. However, it is possible to expand the ground state as a restricted sum of determinantal functions. Configuration interaction can then be admitted and a better ground state wave function obtained. The basis functions used may be either those which are the solution of the one-determinant self-consistent approximation or else those which are the solution of some other problem, for example the Hückel orbitals. If self-consistent orbitals are used then an important consequence follows: there is no interaction between determinants which differ in the assignment of only one electron, i.e. those configurations which correspond to single electron excitations from the Hartree–Fock ground state. This statement is known as Brillouin's theorem and was proved by him in connexion with configuration interaction in atomic systems.

In the next chapter we shall use configuration interaction as an alternative approach for obtaining the self-consistent field solution.

References

Amos, A. T. & Hall, G. G. (1961). *Molec. Phys.* **4**, 25.
Brickstock, A. & Pople, J. A. (1954). *Trans. Faraday Soc.* **50**, 901.
Brown, R. D. & Heffernan, M. L. (1958). *Trans. Faraday Soc.* **54**, 757.
Brown, R. D. & Heffernan, M. L. (1959). *Aust. J. Chem.* **12**, 554.
Dewar, M. J. S. (1949). "Electronic Theory of Organic Chemistry." Oxford University Press, London.
Fischer-Hjalmers, I. (1962). *Ark. Fys.* **21**, 123.
Goeppart-Mayer, M. & Sklar, A. L. (1938). *J. chem. Phys.* **6**, 645.
Hall, G. G. (1954). *Trans. Faraday Soc.* **50**, 773.
Kolboe, S. & Pullman, A. (1958). "Colloque International sur le calcul des functions d'onde moleculaire." C.N.R.S., Paris.
Lowdin, P. O. (1951). *J. chem. Phys.* **18**, 365.
McClelland, B. J. (1961). *Trans. Faraday Soc.* **57**, 2073.
McWeeny, R. (1951). *J. chem. Phys.* **19**, 1614.
McWeeny, R. (1955). *Proc. R. Soc.* **A227**, 288.
McWeeny, R. (1956). *Proc. R. Soc.* **A235**, 496; **A237**, 335.
McWeeny, R. (1959). *Phys. Rev.* **114**, 1528.
McWeeny, R. & Peacock, T. E. (1957). *Proc. phys. Soc.* **A70**, 41.
Mataga, N. & Nishimoto, K. (1957). *Z. phys. Chem.* **13**, 140.
Mulliken, R. S. (1949). *J. Chim. phys.* **46**, 497.
Mulliken, R. S. (1955). *J. chem. Phys.* **23**, 1833, 1841, 2338, 2343.
Mulliken, R. S., Rieke, C. A., Orloff, D. & Orloff, H. (1949). *J. chem. Phys.* **17**, 510.
Pariser, R. & Parr, R. G. (1953). *J. chem. Phys.* **21**, 466, 767.
Peacock, T. E. (1957). *Trans. Faraday Soc.* **53**, 1042.
Peacock, T. E. (1959). *J. chem. Soc.* 3241.
Peacock, T. E. (1959). *J. chem. Soc.* 3645.
Peacock, T. E. (1960a). *Molec. Phys.* **3**, 453.
Peacock, T. E. (1960b). *J. chem. Soc.* 1946.
Peacock, T. E. (1961). *Proc. phys. Soc.* **78**, 460.
Peacock, T. E. & Wilkinson, P. T. (1962). *Proc. phys. Soc.* **79**, 105.
Peacock, T. E. & Wilkinson, P. T. (1964a). *Proc. phys. Soc.* **83**, 355.
Peacock, T. E. (1964b). *Proc. phys. Soc.* **83**, 525.
Pople, J. A. (1953). *Trans. Faraday Soc.* **49**, 1376.
Sidman, J. W. (1957). *J. chem. Phys.* **27**, 429.
Slater, J. C. (1930). *Phys. Rev.* **36**, 57.

CHAPTER 6

Molecular Ground States

Before discussing the calculation of ground state properties it is necessary to discuss a further method which can be used to calculate ground state wave functions. In the last chapter we saw how the iterative solution of the self-consistent field problem leads to a better approximation of the ground state wave function than the Hückel approach. Such methods become tedious when large numbers of electrons are involved. As was pointed out in the last section of Chapter 5 the wave function is defective since it is only a one-determinant approximation. A better wave function is one in which the ground state is written as a linear combination of determinants each having the same symmetry as the ground state. We shall now examine this approach.

1. The Many-determinant Approximation

Consider a wave function of the type

$$\Psi_A = \sum_A c_{iA} \Phi_A \qquad (1)$$

where the Φ_A are determinantal functions which are built out of some arbitrary basis set. In fact in our case these functions will be either Hückel orbitals or self-consistent field orbitals. The functions chosen are those which differ from the one-determinant ground state function in the assignment of one or two electrons. All higher configurations do not interact with the ground state.

Having chosen a set of configurations it is then necessary to compute the matrix elements of the Hamiltonian.

Consider the first two configuration or determinantal functions in (1), let them have the form

$$\Phi_0 = |\psi_1(1)\,\alpha\psi_1(2)\,\beta(2)\ldots\psi_{N/2}(N-1)\,\alpha(N-1)\,\psi_{N/2}(N)\,\beta(N)| \qquad (2)$$

and

$$\Phi_A = \Big|\psi_1(1)\,\alpha\psi_1(2)\,\beta(2)\ldots$$
$$\psi_{N/2}(N-1)\,\psi_{(N/2)+1}(N)\frac{1}{\sqrt{2}}\Big\{\alpha(N-1)\,\beta(N)-\beta(N-1)\,\alpha(N)\Big\} \qquad (3)$$

(2) corresponds to the ground state wave function in the one deter-

minant approximation and (3) to that configuration in which one electron has been excited from the ground state orbital $\psi_{N/2}$ to an orbital $\psi_{(N/2)+1}$ which is unoccupied in the ground state.

The element of the Hamiltonian between these two functions is

$$h_{0A} = \int \Phi_0^* h \Phi_A \, d\tau \tag{4}$$

If our basis orbitals are self-consistent then a simple result follows

$$\begin{aligned} \int \Phi_0^* h \Phi_A \, d\tau &= \sqrt{2} \int \psi_{N/2}^* h \psi_{(N/2)+1} \, dv \\ &= \sqrt{2} E_{(N/2)+1} \int \psi_{N/2}^* \psi_{(N/2)+1} \, d\tau = 0 \end{aligned} \tag{5}$$

This result, that the matrix element of the Hamiltonian between determinants which differ only in orbital is zero when self-consistent orbitals are used, is known as Brillouin's theorem. This theorem was enunciated by Brillouin in connexion with self-consistent field wave function for atoms (1934).

If then a basis of self-consistent field molecular orbitals is used to calculate a many-determinant wave function then only those determinants which differ in the assignment of two electrons can interact. This at once gives a method to improve a one-determinant self-consistent field solution. Further, as stated above, only those determinants which correspond to configurations having the same symmetry will interact, since it can be shown by group theory that the matrix element $\int \psi_i^* h \psi_j \, dv$ is non-vanishing only if ψ_i and ψ_j both contain an irreducible representation of the point group in common. This requirement reduces the number of configurations which can interact even further.

When the matrix elements of the Hamiltonian have been evaluated, the corresponding eigenvalue problem is solved in the usual way. This involves solving the determinant

$$|h_{AB} - E| = 0$$

The lowest eigenvalue is the energy of the ground state and the associated eigenfunction is the wave function of the ground state in the many-configuration approximation. Higher eigenvalues and eigenfunctions give the energies and the wave functions for the excited states of the molecule.

It is found that even when self-consistent orbitals are used a considerable depression of the ground state can occur through the introduction of configuration interaction. Depressions of the order of 2 or 3 eV are not uncommon.

2. Hückel Orbitals and Singly Excited Configurations

Pariser (1956a) has calculated the ground state wave functions for the lower polyacenes using configurations constructed from a set of Hückel molecular orbitals, including those configurations which differ from the ground state by the excitation of a single electron. Inclusion of these configurations results in a lowering of 0·0246 eV in the energy of the ground state of naphthalene. In benzene there is no interaction between the ground state and the singly excited configurations since the molecular orbitals in benzene are determined completely by symmetry. In the higher polyacenes energy depressions in the ground state are of about the same order as for naphthalene. The depressions are 0·0501, 0·0543 and 0·0552 eV for anthracene, naphthalene and pentacene respectively.

In the last section we discussed Brillouin's theorem. If there is no interaction between ground state and singly excited configurations when self-consistent orbitals are used to construct the configurational functions then one-electron properties of the ground state should have the same value in the self-consistent and many-determinant approximation (when only singly excited configurations are used). Such a numerical comparison has been made for naphthalene (Peacock & Wilkinson, 1964). In Table 26 the bond orders for naphthalene using various approximations are listed. In the first row the Hückel bond orders are given, in the second row the bond orders in the many-configuration approximation (taken from Pariser (1956a) and in the third row those calculated in the self-consistent field one-determinant approximation using the same integrals as Pariser (Peacock & Wilkinson, 1964).

TABLE 26. Bond orders for naphthalene in several approximations (for numbering of atoms see Fig. 35)

Bond	12	9,10	23	19
Hückel	0·7246	0·5182	0·6032	0·5547
Many-configuration approx.	0·7434	0·5488	0·5867	0·5353
SCF	0·7453	0·5488	0·5832	0·5352

It can be seen from the table that the values for the bond orders in the last two rows agree to one or two in the third figure. Since the calculations are probably only accurate to this degree it can be seen that in fact the two approximations are equivalent.

3. Inclusion of Doubly Excited Configurations

When configurations are included which differ from the ground state by the assignment of two electrons the matrix elements become somewhat more complicated.

Consider the three configurations

$$|\phi_A(1)\,\alpha(1)\,\phi_A(2)\,\beta(2)\ldots \phi_I(i)\,\alpha(i)\,\phi_I(j)\,\beta(j)\,\phi_{N/2}(n-1)\,\alpha(n-1)\,\phi_{N/2}(n)\,\beta(n)| \quad (6)$$

$$|\phi_A(1)\,\alpha(1)\,\psi_A(2)\,\beta(2)\ldots \phi_{N/2}(n-1)\,\alpha(n-1)\,\psi_{N/2}(n)\,\beta(n)\,\phi_J(i)\,\alpha(1)\,\phi_J(j)\,\beta(j)| \quad (7)$$

$$|\phi_A(1)\,\alpha(1)\,\phi_A(2)\,\beta(2)\ldots \phi_{N/2}(n-1)\,\alpha(n-1)\,\phi_{N/2}(n)\,\beta(n)\,\phi_J(i)\,\psi_K(j)\,\frac{1}{\sqrt{2}}\{(\alpha(i)\,\beta(j)-\beta(i)\,\alpha(j)\}| \quad (8)$$

(6) is the ground state configuration in which the lowest $N/2$ orbitals are doubly occupied, (7) is that in which two electrons are excited from a molecular orbital I to a molecular orbital J, (8) that in which two electrons are excited from I to different orbitals J and K.

This is the greatest extent to which configurations can interact. Configurations which differ from the ground state in the assignment of three or more electrons cannot interact.

The classical paper on extensive configuration interaction is that of Parr, Craig & Ross (1950). In this work the ground and lower excited states of benzene were calculated using non-empirical values of the integrals. All configuration which differed from the ground state in the assignment of one or two electrons were included. Since the molecular orbitals are determined completely by symmetry there is no self-consistent problem to solve. The Hartree–Fock Hamiltonian can be set up from the Hückel charges and bond orders. Because of this there is no interaction between the ground state and the singly excited configurations. There is however considerable interaction between the ground state and the doubly excited configurations. This leads to a depression in the energy of the ground state of 2·7 eV.

The matrix elements for the interaction between the ground state and configurations of type (7) and (8) are

$$H_{6,7} = (IJ)^{\dagger}\,(\gamma)\,(IJ) \quad (9)$$

$$H_{6,8} = \sqrt{2}(IK)^{\dagger}\,(\gamma)\,(IL) \quad (10)$$

4. Applications to Large Aromatic Molecules

Large aromatic molecules occur as graphitic fragments in pyrolytic graphites and in other materials. Graphite itself, considered as an infinite two-dimensional sheet, is the logical upper limit of an aromatic molecule. We shall now discuss the application of molecular SCF theory to graphite.

Wallace (1947) made a Hückel-type calculation on graphite but did not calculate such things as bond orders and other molecular properties. Coulson & Taylor (1952) gave the first numerical evaluation of the bond order between nearest neighbours. Peacock & McWeeny (1959) reported a self-consistent calculation of the π-band of graphite and gave bond orders up to those between third nearest neighbours.

The method used is a straightforward extension of that discussed in the last chapter. The graphite "molecule" is shown diagrammatically in Fig. 39.

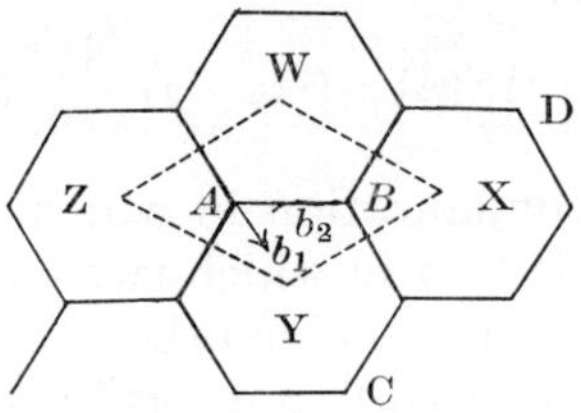

FIG. 39. The graphite molecule.

The unit of structure $WXYZ$ contains two atoms A and B. The orbitals have the usual Bloch form

$$\Phi_A = \frac{1}{\sqrt{N}} \sum_x \exp(i.k.r_{xA})\phi(r-r_{xA}) \tag{11}$$

$$\Phi_B = \frac{1}{\sqrt{N}} \sum_y \exp(i.k.r_{jB}\phi(r-r_{yB}) \tag{12}$$

where the $\phi(r)$ is the orthogonalized $2p_z$-orbital formed out of the carbon $2p$-orbitals in the usual way. The suffices x and y run from 1 to N, where N is the number of structure units in the lattice. $\mathbf{k}$ is a vector which is 2π times a vector $\mathbf{b}$ in the reciprocal lattice space (i.e. k space corresponds closely to the momentum space). These Bloch orbitals (11) and (12) are of course only a general type of symmetry orbital such as we used earlier. The molecular orbitals or crystal orbitals have the form

$$\Psi_k = C_A \Phi_A + C_B \Phi_B \tag{13}$$

where C_A and C_B are constants whose values must be determined from the secular equations. The elements of the Hamiltonian are given by

$$\int \Phi_A^* h \Phi_B dv = h_{AA} = \alpha = h_{BB} \tag{14}$$

and

$$h_{AB} = \int \Phi_A^* h \Phi_B dv = \sigma_1\beta_1 + \sigma_2\beta_2 + \sigma_3\beta_3 + \ldots + g \tag{15}$$

where σ_1, σ_2 and σ_3 are structure sums corresponding to all lattice points of types B, C and D about A respectively and β_1, β_2 and β_3 are the elements of the Hamiltonian ($h_{xA,yB}$) corresponding to bonds AB, AC and AD respectively. The structure sum σ_1 has the form

$$\exp(ik.0)\left[\exp(ik_x a)\exp(ik_y.0)+\exp\left(-i\frac{k_x}{\sqrt{2}}\frac{a}{2}\right)\exp\left(ik_y\frac{\sqrt{3}a}{2}\right)\right.$$
$$\left.+\exp\left(-i\frac{k_x}{\sqrt{2}}\frac{a}{2}\right)\exp\left(-ik_y\frac{\sqrt{3}a}{2}\right)\right] \quad (16)$$

where y runs over all nearest neighbours of atom A. This becomes on simplifying the exponentials

$$\exp(ik_x a)+\exp\left(-ik_x\frac{a}{2}\right)\times 2\cos k_y\frac{\sqrt{3}}{2}a \quad (17)$$

The other structure sums may be evaluated in the same manner. The β_1, β_2 and β_3 are defined in the usual fashion as discussed in the last chapter. The energies of the crystal orbitals are then determined by solution of the secular determinant and have the form

$$\epsilon_k = \alpha \pm |g| \quad (k = 1 \rightarrow N) \quad (18)$$

The "orbital" energies are thus dependent on the value of **k**. Since there are $2N$-electrons the lowest N orbitals are occupied. This means that the first Brillouin zone is filled. The values of C_A and C_B can be obtained in the usual fashion. The bond orders can then be obtained by summing the products of coefficients between the chosen atoms r and s over all occupied molecular orbitals and multiplying by two, to take into account double occupation of each orbital. From this we obtain

$$P_{xA,xA} = P_{xx} = P_{yB,yB} = P_{yy} = 1 \quad (19)$$

$$P_{xA,x'A} = P_{yB,y'B} = P_{xx'} = P_{yy'} = 1 \quad (20)$$

and

$$\left.\begin{aligned} P_1 &= 0{\cdot}5268-0{\cdot}0748\beta_2^2/\beta_1^2 \\ P_2 &= -0{\cdot}2140+0{\cdot}1498\beta_2/\beta_1-0{\cdot}3170\beta_3/\beta_1+0{\cdot}3052\beta_2^2/\beta_1^2 \\ P_3 &= -0{\cdot}0502-0{\cdot}1586\beta_2/\beta_1+0{\cdot}3170\beta_3/\beta_1-0{\cdot}1538\beta_2^2/\beta_1^2 \end{aligned}\right\} \quad (21)$$

The β_i ($=\beta_i^0-\frac{1}{2}P_i\gamma_i$) and P_i are interdependent and we make them self-consistent in the usual way. It is found that the self-consistent values are

$$P_1 = 0{\cdot}525, \quad P_2 = -0{\cdot}223, \quad P_3 = -0{\cdot}037$$

and

$$\beta_1 = 0{\cdot}895\beta, \quad \beta_2 = -0{\cdot}116\beta, \quad \beta_3 = -0{\cdot}015\beta$$

The method then for this case is formally identical with that for any aromatic hydrocarbon but certain modifications occur due to the size of the molecule.

5. Bond Orders and Bond Lengths

In Chapter 2, Section 7, we discussed the relationship between bond length and bond order. It was seen that there was a semi-quantitative relationship between the two. It is expected that such a relationship should hold for bond orders defined in the same way using SCF molecular orbitals. Is the relationship obtained more quantitative than that using the Hückel orbitals? Such a comparison was made by Pritchard & Sumner (1955) who calculated bond lengths from bond orders obtained as a result of several approximations and compared them with experiment.

The correlation was obtained from the equation used in Hückel theory (Coulson, 1939) which was given in (2.11). The results for naphthalene and anthracene are given in Table 27.

TABLE 27. Bond lengths for naphthalene and anthracene

	Bond			
	1–2	2–3	3–8	1–10
Naphthalene				
Hückel (Å)	1·337	1·410	1·417	1·400
SCF (Å)	1·364	1·424	1·396	1·418
Experimental (Å)	1·365	1·425	1·393	1·404

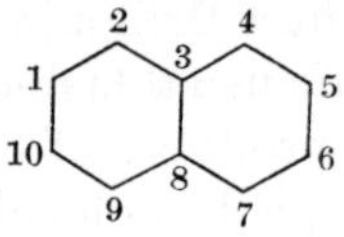

	Bond				
	1–2	2–3	3–4	3–12	1–14
Anthracene					
Hückel (Å)	1·375	1·414	1·400	1·424	1·404
SCF (Å)	1·357	1·438	1·395	1·412	1·431
Experimental (Å)	1·371	1·424	1·396	1·436	1·408

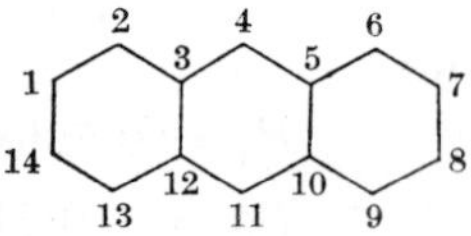

It can be seen that whilst some improvement occurs for naphthalene the predicted bond lengths for anthracene are worse than those predicted using the Hückel theory. This result is quite general. The use of self-consistent orbitals gives no real improvement in the quantitative prediction of bond lengths. However, the semi-quantitative agreement between the quantities still holds in SCF theory.

Amos & Hall (1960) looked for such a relationship between the bond lengths of some nitrogen heterocyclic molecules and the bond orders obtained from self-consistent theory. The same result was found that even here, where there are net charges on the atoms, a semi-quantitative relationship holds between bond length and bond order.

6. Dipole Moments

The calculation of dipole moments was discussed in Chapter 2, Section 10. The theory using SCF molecular orbitals is the same as that for Hückel theory. Amos & Hall (1960) have calculated the dipole moments of a series of heterocyclic aromatics using the SCF charge distribution. They have fixed the σ-bond moments and the lone-pair contribution with respect to pyridine as reference molecule and calculated the π-moments for the other molecules from π-electron data. The π-electron moments are of the order 0·4–0·5 D. The total predicted moments and the experimental moments are given in Table 28.

TABLE 28. Dipole moments of some nitrogen heterocyclics taken from Amos & Hall (1960)

	Predicted moment	Experimental moment (D)
Pyridine	(2·15)	2·15
Pyrimidine	2·13	2·10
Pyridazine	3·79	3·94
Quinoline	2·20	2·16
Acridine	2·29	1·95

It can be seen from these results that the SCF theory tends to predict moments which are in reasonable agreement with experiment. Using the variable electronegativity method, Brown & Heffernan (1959) have estimated the moment of pyridine. They have used five differing forms of their theory and obtained moments between 2·49 and 2·58 D. This compares with the Hückel value given in Table 5 and 2·2 D (Davies, 1955).

One important defect here may be the assumption of orthogonalized atomic orbitals in the self-consistent calculation and the ignoring of this when calculating the moment. In other words the charges and bond orders obtained in the SCF calculation should be transformed into the corresponding quantities in a basis of ordinary $2p$-orbitals as discussed in the last chapter. It has been found (in some unpublished work by the present author) that this has little effect on the value obtained giving a correction of about one unit in the second decimal place.

Before further progress can be made in the prediction of dipole moments it seems that an improved σ-electron theory will have to be formulated. However, the reasonable agreement which Hall and Amos found certainly encourages an optimistic view of the value of the SCF theory.

7. Diamagnetic Susceptibility

In Chapter 2, Section 12, the London theory of the diamagnetic susceptibility of aromatic molecules was discussed. Whilst the theory given was fairly adequate for the discussion of the anisotropy of the polyacene series it is found to be defective when one attempts to discuss the susceptibility of the heterocyclic molecules. The theory has been reformulated in the framework of the self-consistent theory (Davies, 1961).

Certain changes occur when the method discussed in Chapter 2, Section 12, is adapted for use with SCF theory. As was indicated there, a suitable atomic orbital to use is (2.32)

$$\phi_r(\mathbf{r}-\mathbf{R}_r) = \phi_r(\mathbf{r}-\mathbf{R}_r)\exp(2\pi i\alpha\mathbf{R}_r.\mathbf{A}) \tag{22}$$

where $\alpha = e/hc$, $\mathbf{r}$ represents the co-ordinates of the electrons and $\mathbf{R}_r$ the co-ordinates of the rth atom. The basic SCF quantities ω_r and β_{rs} then become

$$\tilde{\omega}_r^L = \int \tilde{\phi}_r^* \mathscr{H}_0 \tilde{\phi}_r\, dv = \int \phi_r^* \mathscr{H}_0 \phi_r\, dv = \omega_r \tag{23}$$

$$\beta_{rs}^L = \int \tilde{\phi}_r^* \mathscr{H}_0 \tilde{\phi}_s\, dv = \epsilon_{rs} \int \phi_r^* \mathscr{H}_0 \phi_s\, dv = \epsilon_{rs}\beta_{rs} \tag{24}$$

where

$$\epsilon_{rs} = \exp \pi i\alpha(\mathbf{R}_r-\mathbf{R}_s).\mathbf{r}\times\tilde{\mathbf{H}} \tag{25}$$

Another expression for ϵ_{rs} was given in (2.35) which leads to

$$\epsilon_{rs} = \exp 2\pi i\alpha\tilde{H}S_{rs} \tag{26}$$

where S_{rs} is the area of the triangle formed by the atoms r and s and the origin.

The elements of the two-electron interaction matrix $(ij|g|rs)$ are unaffected by this transformation of atomic orbitals when only the Coulomb integrals γ_{ij} are regarded as non-vanishing and the basis set form an orthogonal set. The off-diagonal elements of the Hamiltonian become

$$\mathbf{H}_{rs}^L = \epsilon_{rs}\beta_{rs} - \tfrac{1}{2}\tilde{P}_{rs}\gamma_{rs} \quad (r \neq s) \tag{27}$$

In general the charge and bond order matrix $\tilde{P}$ will differ from P.

Consider now the effect of the first-order perturbation term in the Hamiltonian

$$\mathscr{H}' = \sum_i \frac{e^2 \tilde{H}^2}{8mc^2}(x_i^2+y_i^2) \tag{28}$$

The elements of the Hamiltonian, including both the modification of the basis orbitals and the field-dependent Hamiltonian, become

$$\tilde{\mathscr{H}}_{rr} = \tilde{\omega}_r + \tfrac{1}{2}P_{rr}\gamma_{rr} + \sum_{l\neq r}(P_{11}-Z_1)\gamma_{lr} \tag{29}$$

$$\tilde{\mathscr{H}}_{rs} = \beta_{rs} - \tfrac{1}{2}P_{rs}\gamma_{rs} \quad (r \neq s) \tag{30}$$

where

$$\tilde{\omega}_r = \omega_r + \tilde{M}_{rr}$$

$$\tilde{\beta}_{rs} = \epsilon_{rs}\beta_{rs} + \tilde{M}_{rs} \tag{31}$$

and

$$M_{rs} = \frac{e^2 \tilde{H}^2}{8mc^2}\int \phi_r^*(1)(x_i^2+y_i^2)\tilde{\phi}_s(i)\,d\tau_i = \epsilon_{rs}M_{rs} \tag{32}$$

A scheme for carrying out a calculation would be as follows. As a first approximation write

$$\left.\begin{aligned}\tilde{\omega}_r &= \omega_r\\ \tilde{\beta}_{rs} &= \epsilon_{rs}\beta_{rs}\\ \tilde{P}_{rs} &= P_{rs}\end{aligned}\right\} \tag{33}$$

The susceptibility obtained in this way will be the equivalent to the London susceptibility. The **P** matrix may be chosen as that of the field-free SCF calculation. The solving of the resultant eigenvalue problem presents some difficulties as the Hamiltonian is no longer symmetric but Hermitian symmetric with imaginary off-diagonal elements. The straightforward approach is to use a diagonalization method and such a technique is discussed by Davies in his paper.

Improvements to the value obtained can be made by using equations (29), (30) and (31).

Davies obtains values of $-41{\cdot}36$ and $-39{\cdot}86$ for the π-electron susceptibilities for benzene and pyridine. These compare with a value of $-41{\cdot}2$ for the susceptibility of benzene. A reliable value for pyridine is not known. The SCF theory would appear to be in good agreement with experiment in the one case where the direct comparison is possible.

8. Conclusion

It appears that the use of SCF theory leads to some improvement in the prediction of molecular properties. Dipole moments and diamagnetic susceptibilities both seem to be given better in the SCF theory. There is, however, little improvement in the correlation and bond orders and bond lengths. It is also found that there is no improvement in either ionization potentials or resonance energies in the self-consistent field theory.

The one property remaining of those discussed in Chapter 2 is electronic spectra. The whole of the next chapter will be devoted to a discussion of the calculation of electronic spectra using self-consistent molecular orbitals and configuration interaction. It is in the prediction of electronic spectra that SCF theory has had its greatest success.

References

Amos, A. T. & Hall, G. G. (1960). *Molec. Phys.* **4**, 25.
Brillouin, L. (1934). *Actual. scient. ind.* no. 159.
Brown, R. D. & Heffernan, M. L. (1959). *Aus. J. Chem.* **12**, 554.
Coulson, C. A. (1939). *Proc. R. Soc.* **A169**, 413.
Coulson, C. A. & Taylor, R. (1952). *Proc. phys. Soc.* **A65**, 815.
Davies, D. W. (1955). *Trans. Faraday Soc.* **51**, 449.
Davies, D. W. (1961). *Trans. Faraday Soc.* **57**, 2081.
Pariser, R. (1956a). *J. chem. Phys.* **24**, 250.
Pariser, R. (1956b). *J. chem. Phys.* **25**, 1112.
Parr, R. G., Craig, D. P. & Ross, I. G. (1950). *J. chem. Phys.* **18**, 1561.
Peacock, T. E. & McWeeny, R. (1959). *Proc. phys. Soc.* **74**, 385.
Peacock, T. E. & Wilkinson, P. T. (1964). *Proc. phys. Soc.* **83**, 525.
Pritchard, H. O. & Sumner, F. H. (1955). *Trans. Faraday Soc.* **51**, 457.
Wallace, P. R. (1947). *Phys. Rev.* **36**, 57.

CHAPTER 7

Electronic Spectra—I

1. Introduction

In Chapter 2 the use of the Hückel theory in calculating electronic spectra was discussed. Even in its most sophisticated form (i.e. with inclusion of configuration interaction) the method often gives poor results when compared with experiment. Much work has recently been done on the calculation of spectra using semi-empirical methods and various adaptations of them.

In these methods, a Hartree–Fock Hamiltonian is considered, wave functions are set up for the ground state and the excited state molecular orbital configurations, and total π-electron energies are evaluated. Matters are improved further by allowing functions of like symmetry but in general from different configurations to interact. Unfortunately, the results of such calculations have on the whole been extremely disappointing.

More recently these methods have been revised (Moffitt, 1954; Pariser & Parr, 1953) non-empirical evaluation of the dominant integrals being replaced by estimations based on ionization potential and electron affinity data (see Chapter 5). Apart from easing the mathematical difficulties such procedures allow in some measure for effects which can be distinguished physically (e.g. electron correlation, polarization of the framework) but which cannot be introduced satisfactorily non-empirically. So much simplification is achieved by the usual approximation $(rs|g|tu) = \delta_{rt}\delta_{su}\gamma_{rs}$ that many configuration calculations using SCF orbitals present very little difficulty especially when modern high-speed electronic computers are used. Calculations have been carried out on many hydrocarbons and also on a wide range of heterocyclic aromatic molecules.

2. The Transition Energy

The possible one-determinant functions for a system in which an electron has been excited from ψ_i to ψ_j are

$$\Phi = \left| \psi_1(1)\,\alpha(1)\ldots\psi_{i-1}(N-2)\,\beta(N-2) \begin{cases} \psi_i(N-1)\,\alpha(N-1)\,\psi_j(N)\,\alpha(N) \\ \psi_i(N-1)\,\alpha(N-1)\,\psi_j(N)\,\beta(N) \\ \psi_i(N-1)\,\beta(N-1)\,\psi_j(N)\,\beta(N) \end{cases} \right|$$
$$\psi_i(N-1)\,\beta(N-1)\,\psi_j(N)\,\beta(N)$$

The four wave functions have all to be considered and lead to the usual singlet and triplet states whose wave functions are linear combinations of the above and are

$$^{1}\Phi_{ij} = \left| \psi_1(1)\,\alpha(1)\ldots\psi_{i-1}(N-2)\,\beta(N-2)\,\psi_i(N-1)\,\psi_j(N) \right.$$

$$\left. \frac{1}{\sqrt{2}}(\alpha(N-1)\,\beta(N)) - (\beta(N-1)\,\alpha(N)) \right| \tag{1}$$

and

$$^{3}\Phi_{ij} = \left| \psi_1(1)\,\alpha(1)\ldots\psi_{i-1}(N-2)\,\beta(N-2)\,\psi_i(N-1)\,\psi_j(N) \right.$$

$$\left. \begin{cases} \alpha(N-1)\,\alpha(N) \\ \frac{1}{\sqrt{2}}(\alpha(N-1)\,\beta(N)+\beta(N-1)\,\alpha(N)) \\ \beta(N-1)\,\beta(N) \end{cases} \right| \tag{2}$$

which lead to energies for the two states of

$$E(^{1,\,3}\Phi_{ij}) = \int {}^{1,3}\Phi_{ij}\,H\,{}^{1,\,3}\Phi_{ij}\,d\tau = 2\sum_{n\neq i,\,j} f_n + f_i + f_j + \sum_{n,\,m\neq i}(2J_{mn}-K_{mn})$$

$$+ \sum_{n\neq i,\,j}(2J_{in}-K_{in}) + \sum_{n\neq i,\,j}(2J_{nj}-K_{nj}) + J_{ij} \pm K_i \tag{3}$$

where the plus sign holds for the singlet and the minus sign for the triplet state.

The transition energy $E(^{1,\,3}\Phi_{ij}) - E(\Phi_0)$ is then

$$f_j - f_i + \sum_n (2J_{nj}-K_{nj}) - \sum_n (2J_{in}-K_{in}) - (J_{ij}-K_{ij}) \pm K_{ij} \tag{4}$$

which gives in the LCAO approximation

$$\epsilon_j - \epsilon_i - (J_{ij}-K_{ij}) \pm K_{ij} \tag{5}$$

where the ϵ_j and ϵ_i are the orbital energies of electrons in ψ_i and ψ_j.

If we let (A), $(B)\ldots$ denote the columns of atomic orbital coefficients representing the molecular orbitals $A, B \ldots$ and (AB) the column matrix whose nth element is $A_n B_n$, then (5) becomes

$$^{1,\,3}E_{I=J} = (I \rightarrow J|H|I \rightarrow J)$$

$$= \epsilon_J - \epsilon_I - [(II)^{\dagger}(\gamma)\,(JJ) - (IJ)^{\dagger}(\gamma)\,(IJ)] \pm (IJ)^{\dagger}(\gamma)\,(IJ) \tag{6}$$

where (γ) is the matrix of atomic Coulomb integrals γ_{rs}.

3. The Configuration Interaction Problem

Dewar & Longuet-Higgins (1954) found that a satisfactory interpretation of the ultra-violet spectrum of alternant hydrocarbons can be obtained using all single excitations involving the top two filled and the bottom two empty molecular orbitals. This assumption works well except in the case of the second orbital being degenerate with the third or nearly degenerate, in these cases it is essential to include more configurations. The normal assumptions of using four orbitals gives rise to four configurations for the lower states which may interact in pairs.

$$\Phi_{A\to A'}, \qquad \Phi_{A\to B'}$$
$$\Phi_{B\to B'}, \qquad \Phi_{B\to A'}$$

where A and A' and B and B' refer to those pairs of orbitals which are symmetrical about the energy zero; the ascending energy order of the orbitals is B, A, A' and B'.

It is usually found that these states interact in pairs leading to factorization of the 4×4 determinant into two 2×2 determinants. $\Phi_{A\to A'}$ and $\Phi_{B\to B'}$ constitute one pair and $\Phi_{A\to B'}$ and $\Phi_{B\to A'}$ the other.

Occasionally, due to molecular orbital degeneracies it is necessary to include more configurations as stated above. This is the case with the higher polyacenes and, as will be seen later, it is necessary to include nine configurations. Even in these cases, however, considerable factorization occurs which simplifies the problem.

The off-diagonal elements of the interaction matrix are given by

$$\left.\begin{aligned}
{}^{1,3}(I\to J|H|K\to L) &= -[(IK)^\dagger(\gamma)(JL)-(LK)^\dagger(\gamma)(JI)] \\
&\quad \pm (LK)^\dagger(\gamma)(JI) \\
{}^{1,3}(I\to J|H|I\to L) &= \epsilon_{JL}-[(II)^\dagger(\gamma)(JL)-(LI)^\dagger(\gamma)(JI)] \\
&\quad \pm (LI)^\dagger(\gamma)(JI) \\
{}^{1,3}(I\to J|H|K\to J) &= -\epsilon_{IK}-[(IK)^\dagger(\gamma)(JJ)-(JK)^\dagger(\gamma)(JI)] \\
&\quad \pm (JK)^\dagger(\gamma)(JI)
\end{aligned}\right\} \tag{7}$$

If self-consistent orbitals are used then the ϵ terms vanish in (7).

When self-consistent orbitals are used then there is no interaction between the ground state and any of the excited states. This is a straightforward application of Brillouin's theorem. If, however, self-consistent orbitals had not been used then these terms do not vanish and are found to be (see Chapter 6)

$${}^1(0|H|I\to J) = \sqrt{2}(1)^\dagger(h)(J) = \sqrt{2}\epsilon_{ij} \tag{8}$$

4. The Calculation of Orbitals using the SCF Hamiltonian

Equations (6), (7) and (8) require the orbital coefficients for a few of the molecular orbitals of a molecule. These are not obtained explicitly in the density matrix method, but can be obtained quite easily from the Hamiltonian using the "steepest descent" method which is the technique used in the density matrix approach (McWeeny, 1956).

1. Form $\mathbf{hA}_0$ and compute $\epsilon_A^0 = \mathbf{A}_0^\dagger \mathbf{hA}_0$ and write $\mathbf{r}_0 = \mathbf{hA}_0 - \epsilon_A^0 \mathbf{A}_0$.
2. Compute $\mathbf{s}_0 = \mathbf{hr}_0 - \epsilon_A^0 \mathbf{r}_0$ and compute $\lambda_0 = -\mathbf{r}_0^\dagger \mathbf{r}_0 / \mathbf{r}_0^\dagger \mathbf{s}_0$.
3. Then a better approximation is $\mathbf{A}_1 = \mathbf{A}_0 - \lambda_0 \mathbf{r}_0$.

This process converges, but not always to the desired eigenvector, say **B** (this is connected with the position of ϵ_A and ϵ_B on the energy surface). This difficulty is easily overcome by finding the unwanted **B** and then replacing **h** by a modified matrix

$$\mathbf{h}_1 = \mathbf{h} - \epsilon_B \mathbf{B}\mathbf{B}^\dagger$$

A can then be obtained from $\mathbf{h}_1$ without the interference of **B**. This is easily seen; the vector $\mathbf{A}_0$ may be written as a linear combination of the eigenvectors of h, viz.

$$\mathbf{A}_0 = c_A \mathbf{A} + c_B \mathbf{B} + c_C \mathbf{C} + \ldots + c_N \mathbf{N}$$

Operation of $\mathbf{h}_1$ on this gives

$$\begin{aligned}\mathbf{h}_1 \mathbf{A}_0 &= h_1(c_A \mathbf{A} + c_C \mathbf{C} + \ldots c_N \mathbf{N}) + \epsilon_B(\mathbf{hB} - \epsilon_B \mathbf{B}\mathbf{B}^\dagger \mathbf{B}) \\ &= \mathbf{h}_1(c_A \mathbf{A} + c_C \mathbf{C} + \ldots c_N \mathbf{N}) + (\mathbf{hB} - \epsilon_B \mathbf{B}) \\ &= h(c_A \mathbf{A} + \mathbf{c}_C + \ldots c_N \mathbf{N})\end{aligned}$$

the term in **B** disappears because **B** is an eigenvector of **h**. The term $-\epsilon_B \mathbf{B}\mathbf{B}^\dagger$ annihilates everything but $c_B \mathbf{B}$, since $\mathbf{B}^\dagger \mathbf{P} = 0$ $(\mathbf{B} \neq \mathbf{P})$, and therefore does not appear in the final result.

5. The Nitrogen Heterocyclics

The method discussed in the above paragraphs has been applied to the benzene azine and polyazine series. The orbitals used are the self-consistent ones which arise from the calculation discussed in Chapter 5. The molecules pyridine, pyridazine, pyrimidine, pyrazine and *sym*-triazine are considered here. We shall attempt to relate the spectra of the heterocyclic molecules to that of benzene.

The molecular orbitals of benzene are shown diagrammatically in Fig. 40.

In what follows we shall use the transitions occurring between A, B, A' and B'. The four molecular orbitals A, B, A' and B' have the forms shown in Fig. 41.

Those orbitals which have similar forms in the heterocyclic derivatives will be called A, B, A' and B' in the same fashion.

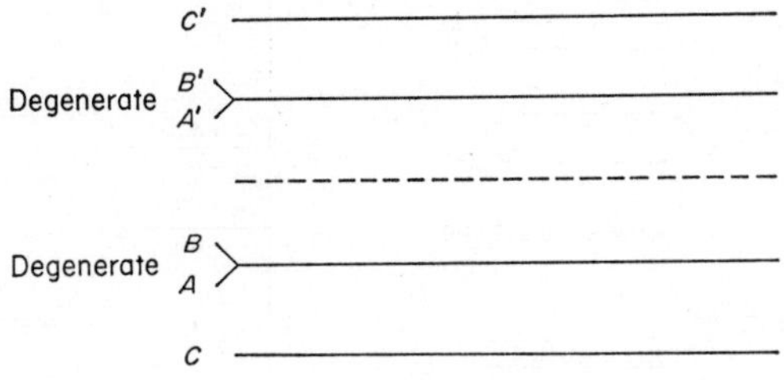

FIG. 40.

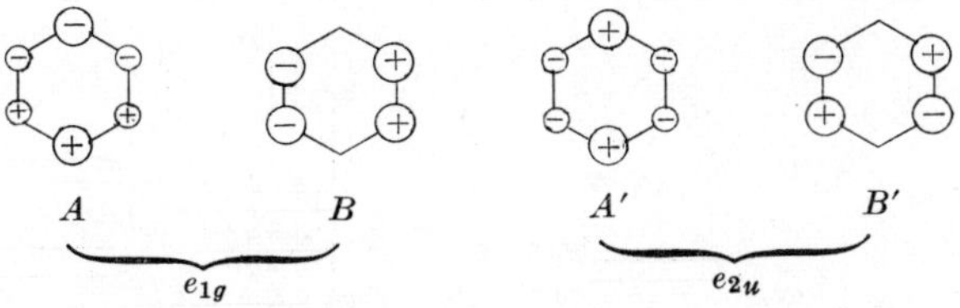

FIG. 41. Molecular orbitals of benzene. (*By permission of the Institute of Physics and the Physical Society.*)

In benzene there is a degeneracy between A and B, and between A' and B'. In the heterocyclic derivatives the following order of orbital energy is followed

Pyridine	A	B	A'	B'
Pyridazine	B	A	B'	A'
Pyrimidine	B	A	B'	A'
Pyrazine	A	B	A'	B'
Triazine	$A = B$		$A' = B'$	

This order can be easily understood, for the energies of A and A' (or of B and B') move in the same way under the perturbation, instead of symmetrically with respect to the energy zero; it is clear that even with initially non-degenerate levels a substantial perturbation could have a similar effect on the sequence of orbital energies. The degeneracies in *sym*-triazine persist for group theoretical reasons, the orbitals A and B and A' and B' forming bases for the two-dimensional representations of the group D_{3h}.

The transition energies of the singlet states corresponding to the transitions $A \rightarrow A'$, $A \rightarrow B'$, $B \rightarrow A'$, and $B \rightarrow B'$ are shown in Fig. 42.

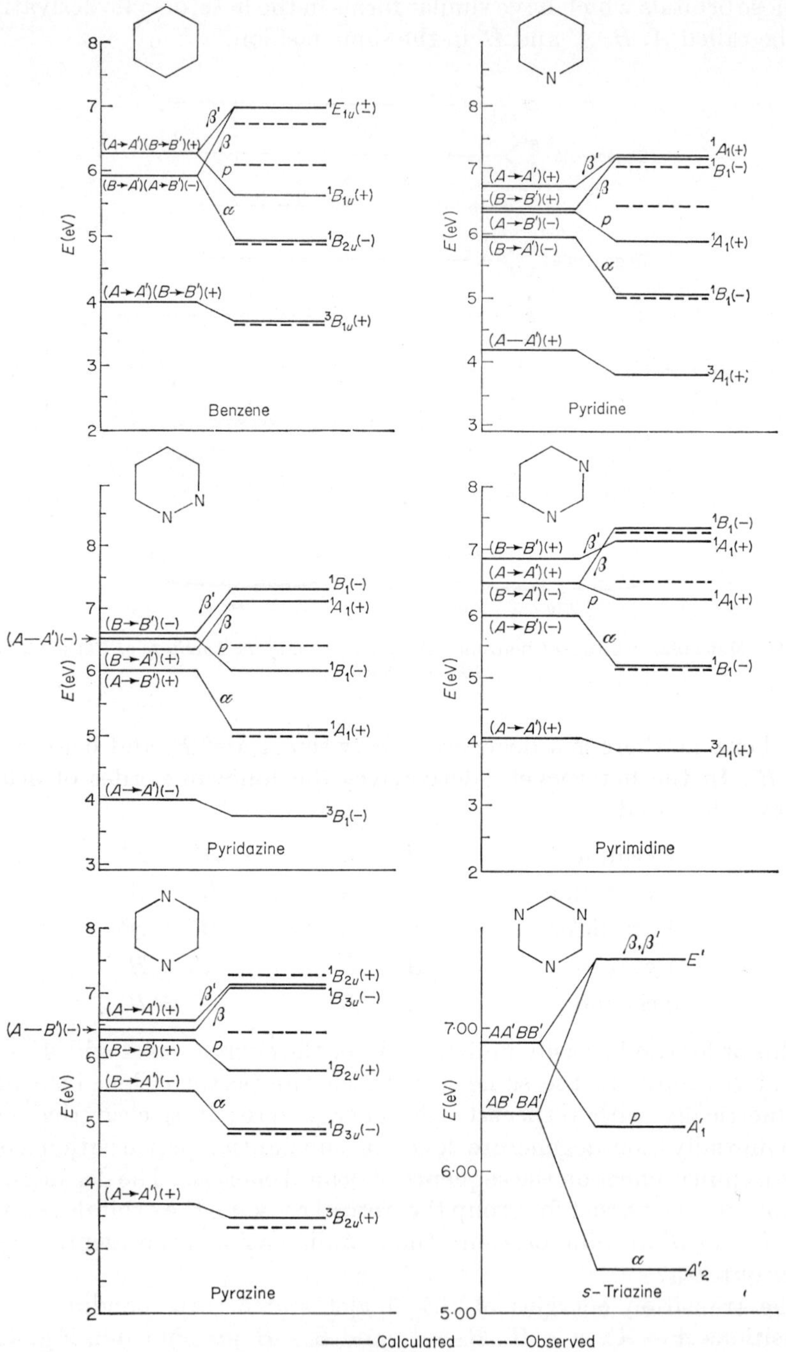

Fig. 42. Excited states of benzene and the azines. (*By permission of the Institute of Physics and the Physical Society.*)

Configuration interaction is then admitted between the four configurations (which interact in pairs leading to factorization of the determinant), and the results are also shown in Fig. 42. The corresponding diagram for benzene is also given. The experimental energies are shown in broken lines and are taken from the data of Klevens & Platt (1949).

The symmetries of the states are shown using the notation of Eyring, Walter & Kimball (1944) and a + or − sign is added to indicate symmetry or antisymmetry with respect to reflection across the out-of-molecule plane of reflection (in pyrazine this is taken to pass through the two nitrogen atoms and in *sym*-triazine the three planes are equivalent).

The first conclusion to be drawn is that the α, p, β and β' bands for the heterocyclic molecules are correlated pictorially with electron jumps between orbitals whose form resemble those of their counterparts in benzene, without regard to their energies, and the alternant character of the parent is the factor responsible for the spectral similarities of benzene and its heterocyclic derivatives.

Secondly, there is an important observation to be made about the importance of configuration interaction. In spite of the absence of degeneracies in the heterocyclics heavy interaction occurs between states wherever it is allowed by symmetry. Configuration interaction should therefore never be ignored simply because degeneracies have been resolved by the introduction of heteroatoms.

Lastly it can be seen that there is reasonable agreement between theory and experiment for the whole series. It appears that the introduction of self-consistency together with configuration interaction, when the elements of the interaction matrix are properly evaluated, lead to a fairly good interpretation of the spectrum. The one state which is significantly different from experiment in all cases is the second lowest singlet state. There are additional complicating factors, related to the state in benzene, which we shall not go into here.

This understanding of the spectra of the azines in terms of that of benzene was given by McWeeny & Peacock (1957) and for triazine by Peacock (1957). Other workers have reached similar conclusions to those reported above, notably Mataga & Nishimoto (1957) who made similar calculations on benzene, pyridine, pyrazine and *sym*-triazine, and Brown & Heffernan (1959) who used the variable electronegativity SCF method in a study of pyridine.

6. The Polyacenes

The spectra of the polyacenes have been the subjects of many papers. Foremost attention has been directed to benzene and naphthalene. SCF calculations including configuration interaction have been carried out by Pople (1955), Pariser & Parr (1953), Kolboe & Pullman (1958), Moser & Brion (1955), Lefebvre & Moser (1956), Peacock (1959) and Peacock & Wilkinson (1964). This is by no means an exhaustive list of the calculations which have been done on the polyacenes.

The self-consistent ground states for the first five members of the polyacene series were discussed in Chapter 5, Section 5. In Table 16 the orbital energies of the molecules are given (as reported in Peacock & Wilkinson, 1964).

In calculating the spectrum of the polyacenes it is necessary to include more than the four configurations discussed above. The reason for this can be seen from an examination of Table 16. In anthracene, naphthacene and pentacene the B and C orbitals and also the B' and C' are near degenerate. For these molecules it is necessary to include the nine configurations which can arise from one-electron jumps between these orbitals. In order to make comparison possible the spectra of the first two members, benzene and naphthalene, were calculated using nine configurations.

The orbital energies of the relevant orbitals are given in Table 29. Here the orbitals are grouped together according to their symmetry properties and given the labels appropriate to the representations of the point

TABLE 29. Molecular orbitals and orbital energies for the polyacenes classified according to the representations of D_{2h}

Symmetry	Benzene		Naphthalene		Anthracene		Naphthacene		Pentacene	
b_{1u}	C	$1{\cdot}845\beta$	B	$1{\cdot}137\beta$	A'	$-0{\cdot}764\beta$	C	$1{\cdot}098\beta$	A'	$-0{\cdot}609\beta$
	B'	$-1{\cdot}178$	C'	$-1{\cdot}382$			B'	$-1{\cdot}032$		
b_{2g}	A	$1{\cdot}178$	A'	$-0{\cdot}922$	B	$1{\cdot}114$	A'	$-0{\cdot}673$	C	$1{\cdot}086$
					C'	$-1{\cdot}185$			B'	$-0{\cdot}917$
b_{3g}	B	$1{\cdot}178$	C	$1{\cdot}382$	A	$0{\cdot}764$	B	$1{\cdot}032$	A	$0{\cdot}609$
	C'	$-1{\cdot}845$	B'	$-1{\cdot}137$			C'	$-1{\cdot}098$		
a_{1u}	A'	$-1{\cdot}178$	A	$0{\cdot}922$	C	$1{\cdot}185$	A	$0{\cdot}673$	B	$0{\cdot}917$
					B'	$-1{\cdot}114$			C'	$-1{\cdot}086$

group D_{2h}. The long molecular axis is chosen as the x-axis and the short axis as the y-axis. The symbol b_{1u} means that the orbital is symmetric to reflection across both the xz and the yz planes, b_{2g} that it is symmetric to reflection across the xz plane but antisymmetric with respect to the yz plane, b_{3g} that it is symmetric with respect to the yz plane and antisymmetric with respect to the xz plane and, finally, a_{1u} that it is antisymmetric with respect to both planes. For comparative purposes benzene is here considered to have the symmetry D_{2h}.

The results of the configuration interaction calculations of the lowest excited singlet states for the molecules considered are given in Table 30.

TABLE 30. Energies, symmetries, wave functions and experimental energies for the first four singlet excited states of the first five polyacenes

	Energy	Symmetry	Wave function	Experimental energy
Benzene	39,563	B_{3u}	$2^{-1/2}[\Phi(B \to A') + \Phi(B \to A')]$	37,900
	44,704	B_{2u}	$2^{-1/2}[\Phi(A \to A') - \Phi(B \to B')]$	48,000
	57,195	B_{3u}	$2^{-1/2}[\Phi(B \to A') - \Phi(A \to B')]$	54,500
	57,197	B_{2u}	$2^{-1/2}[\Phi(A \to A') + \Phi(B \to B')]$	
Naphthalene	35,448	B_{3u}	$2^{-1/2}[\Phi(B \to A') - \Phi(A \to B')]$	31,800
	35,449	B_{2u}	$\Phi(A \to A')$	34,600
	47,972	B_{1g}	$2^{-1/2}[\Phi(C \to A') + \Phi(A \to C')]$	45,500
	50,224	B_{3u}	$2^{-1/2}[\Phi(B \to A') + \Phi(A \to B')]$	52,600
Anthracene	28,738	B_{2u}	$\Phi(A \to A')$	26,400
	33,147	B_{3u}	$2^{-1/2}[\Phi(A \to B') - \Phi(B \to A')]$	—
	38,712	B_{1g}	$2^{-1/2}[\Phi(C \to A') + \Phi(A \to C')]$	39,550
	43,877	B_{1g}	$2^{-1/2}[\Phi(C \to A') - \Phi(A \to C')]$	45,300
Naphthacene	24,822	B_{2u}	$\Phi(A \to A')$	21,200
	32,440	B_{3u}	$2^{-1/2}[\Phi(C \to A') - \Phi(A \to C')]$	—
	33,112	B_{1g}	$2^{-1/2}[\Phi(A \to B') - \Phi(B \to A')]$	36,800
	38,858	B_{1g}	$2^{-1/2}[\Phi(A \to B') + \Phi(B \to A')]$	43,500
Pentacene	22,146	B_{2u}	$\Phi(A \to A')$	17,400
	29,154	B_{1g}	$2^{-1/2}[\Phi(B \to A') + \Phi(A \to B')]$	—
	32,303	B_{3u}	$2^{-1/2}[\Phi(C \to A') - \Phi(A \to C')]$	—
	35,047	B_{1g}	$2^{-1/2}[\Phi(B \to A') - \Phi(A \to B')]$	—

The transition which is correlated with $\Phi(A \to A')$ in Table 30 is the band named by Clar (1941) the *p*-band. The other low-energy band, which Clar called the α-band is correlated with a jump of type $2^{-1/2}$ $(A \to B' + B \to A')$. The higher bands called by Clar β' and β are also associated, one with $B \to B'$ and the other with $B \to A' \pm A \to B'$. Clar made his correlation purely on intensity considerations and it is interesting to note that this classification in fact has a more secure foundation on the transitions between different types of orbitals. Examination of the excited states for the azines shows that the same correlations between the α-, *p*-, β- and β'-bands and electron jumps is present. The α-band is not observed in the molecules higher than naphthalene. The predicted energies are in close agreement with experiment if we leave the α-band out of consideration in anthracene, naphthacene and pentacene.

In Fig. 43 the energy of the p-band is plotted against the number of rings for the series. It is easily seen that the theoretical results predict that the p-band converges to a limit with increasing ring size. In this plot results of calculations on molecules with up to eight rings are used. This convergence has a value of about 18,000$\bar{\nu}$. The experimental curve which is plotted up to the sixth member does not clearly point to any convergence limit. However, as only five members of the series are well known,

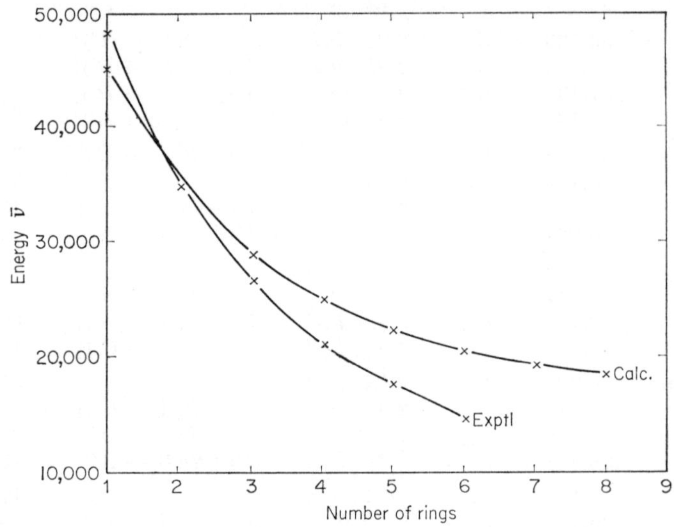

FIG. 43. The p-band for the polyacenes. (*By permission of the Institute of Physics and the Physical Society.*)

and data for the sixth member has only been measured once, it is too early to give a definite answer about convergence. The theoretical curve only shows a definite trend to convergence at five rings.

Finally it is important to note that the use of self-consistent orbitals with some considerable configuration interaction leads to a predicted spectrum which is in good agreement with experiment in all cases.

7. Monosubstituted Benzenes

Calculations of this type have also been carried through by many authors on substituted benzenes in which the substituent can be represented as a conjugated fragment which extends over the whole of the molecule. Such groups are carbonyl, amino, nitrile and nitro. In this section the spectra of such molecules will be discussed on this basis.

In benzonitrile there are two conjugated systems. One of these is in the plane of the benzene ring and includes one $2p$-orbital on carbon and one on the nitrogen atom which form the nitrile group. The other system is composed completely of the $2p$-orbitals of the nitrile group which are at right angles to the main system. The ground state of this molecule was discussed in Chapter 5. The electronic spectrum was calculated by Peacock & Wilkinson (1962). In Table 31 the electronic transitions are listed together with their oscillator strengths and compared with the experimental values.

TABLE 31. Comparison between calculated and observed bands for benzonitrile

	Predicted		Experimental	
	Energy ($\bar{\nu}$)	f	Energy ($\bar{\nu}$)	f
α-band	40,300	0·001	36,200	0·005
p-band	44,700	0·211	44,000	0·088
β'-band	53,900	0·701	52,600	Intense
β-band	55,100	0·505		

It is seen that the predicted spectrum is in excellent agreement with that observed by Platt (1951).

The aniline molecule has been thoroughly studied by Mrs. Fischer-Hjalmars (1962). She has calculated the first six singlet states of aniline. The predicted spectrum is compared with the observed spectrum in Table 32.

TABLE 32. Spectrum of aniline; calculated and observed bands

	Predicted		Observed	
State	Energy (eV)	Intensity	Energy (eV)	Intensity $\log \epsilon_{max}$
B_2	4·699	0·015	4·32	3·1
A_1	5·581	0·19	5·31	3·9
B_2	6·503	0·55	6·32	4·3
A_1	6·668	0·68	7·06	4·5
A_1	7·396	0·41		
B_2	7·496	0·61		

It can be seen once again that there is excellent agreement between theory and experiment.

Sidman (1957) calculated the spectrum of *p*-benzoquinone using the same technique and his results are given in Table 32 together with the experimental data.

TABLE 33. *p*-Benzoquinone

State	Predicted energy (eV)	Observed energy
$^1B_{1g}$	5·7	4·4
$^1B_{1g}$	6·8	
$^1B_{3u}$	6·3	5·1
$^1B_{3u}$	8·3	

The agreement in this case is nothing like as good as it was in the other two cases. However, it is sufficient to understand in a semi-quantitative way the spectrum of benzoquinone.

Looking at these results which are representative of the pattern which has emerged from many calculations, by several authors on a wide range of molecules, it is seen that the self-consistent field theory with limited configuration interaction is able to give a reliable interpretation of the spectra of aromatic molecules.

8. Oscillator Strengths

It is necessary to compare the values of calculated oscillator strengths using orthogonal and non-orthogonal atomic orbital bases. This was discussed in Chapter 5, Section 8, with reference to the atom and bond populations in the ground state.

The oscillator strength for a transition $\Psi_\alpha \to \Psi_\beta$ is given by (Mulliken & Rieke, 1941)

$$f_{\alpha\beta} = 1{\cdot}085 \times 10^{11} \bar{\nu}\, Q_{\alpha\beta}^2$$

where $\bar{\nu}$ is the frequency of the transition (in wave numbers) and $Q_{\alpha\beta}^2$ is given by

$$Q_{\alpha\beta}^2 = Q_{(x)\,\alpha\beta}^2 + Q_{(y)\,\alpha\beta}^2 + Q_{(z)\,\alpha\beta}^2$$

where

$$Q_{x(\alpha\beta)} = e^2 \int \Psi_\alpha^* \sum_{i=1}^{N} x_i \Psi_\beta \, d\tau$$

The contribution to $Q_{x(\alpha\beta)}$ vanishes except between functions Φ and Φ' which differ in only one orbital, e.g. $A \to A'$; the element of Q_x is then given by

$$Q_x = \sqrt{2}\, \mathrm{tr}\, \overline{\mathbf{XP}}_{AA'}$$

where

$$\bar{\mathbf{P}}_{AA'} = \bar{\mathbf{T}}_A \bar{\mathbf{T}}_{A'}^{\dagger} \quad \text{and} \quad \bar{\mathbf{X}}_{rs} = \int \bar{\phi}_r^2 x \phi_s \, dv$$

When we go to the non-orthogonal basis of ordinary $2p$ atomic orbitals, the expression for Q_x becomes

$$Q_x = \sqrt{2}\,\mathrm{tr}\,\overline{\mathbf{XP}}_{AA'}$$

where

$$\mathbf{P}_{AA'} = \mathbf{S}^{-1/2}\bar{\mathbf{P}}\mathbf{S}^{-1/2} \quad \text{and} \quad \mathbf{X}_{rs} = \int \phi_r^* \, x \phi_s \, dv = x_{rs} S_{rs}$$

Since x_{rs} is the centroid of orbital r and x_{rs} that of the centroid of bond r—s, and for ordinary $2p$-orbitals these centroids are at the atom and bond mid-points, the calculation in the non-orthogonal basis is straightforward. It is usual, however, to make similar approximations when calculating transition moments from orbital coefficients which are those appropriate to the orthogonalized atomic orbital basis. Because these orbitals are neither localized nor centrosymmetric there is no real justification for making this assumption. It is useful, therefore, to compare oscillator strengths calculated properly using the ordinary $2p$ atomic orbitals and their coefficients and oscillator strengths calculated using orthogonalized orbitals and making the assumptions discussed above.

In Table 34 these quantities are compared for naphthalene and pyridine

TABLE 34

	Naphthalene			
	α	p	β	β'
Calculated using non-orthogonal AOs	0·000	0·208	2·175	1·025
Calculated by assuming orthogonal AOs and overlap distributions centrosymmetric	0·000	0·205	2·213	1·040
	Pyridine			
	α	p	β	β'
Calculated using non-orthogonal AOs	0·012	0·022	1·264	1·321
Calculated by assuming orthogonal AOs and overlap distributions centrosymmetric	0·009	0·016	1·223	1·302

From Table 34 it can be seen that the values of the oscillator strengths obtained by using the more convenient basis without detailed analysis of the transition charge density agree well with those calculated more rigorously.

9. The Effect of Bond Length Changes

In making calculations of the type described in this chapter, it is frequently assumed that a standard set of one- and two-electron integrals, β and γ_{ij}, calculated for certain mean bond lengths (i.e. the bond length in benzene) can be used. This reduces the amount of labour or the complexity of a computer programme when such a set of standard integrals can be used. It is now necessary to examine this assumption and see if it is justified.

The π-electron ground state energy of a molecule in the self-consistent field theory is given by

$$E = \operatorname{tr}\mathbf{Rh}+\operatorname{tr}\mathbf{Rf} = 2\operatorname{tr}\mathbf{Rf}+\operatorname{tr}\mathbf{RG}$$

It may be recalled that the **f** and **G** matrices are those of the bare framework Hamiltonian and the total electron interaction operator (see Chapter 5).

Consider the variation in energy due to a small change in bond length $r_{ij} \to r\ \ +\delta r$ of the bond i—j.

A. The Change in f_{ij}

To a good approximation it is true that

$$f'_{ij} = S'_{ij} f_{ij}/S_{ij}$$

where S'_{ij} is the overlap integral when the distance i—j is $r_{ij}+\delta r$.

For homonuclear bonds the overlap integral between two $2p$ π-orbitals is given by

$$S = \exp(-\rho/2)\left(1+\frac{\rho}{2}+\frac{\rho^2}{10}+\frac{\rho^3}{120}\right)$$

where $\rho = Zr$, Z is the effective nuclear charge on atoms i and j, and r the interatomic distance (in atomic units). This gives

$$\frac{dS}{dr} = -\exp(-\rho/2)\left(\frac{\rho^2}{20r}+\frac{\rho^3}{40r}+\frac{\rho^4}{240r}\right)$$

The change in the overlap integral S_{ij} due to a small change r_{ij} is given by

$$\delta S_{ij} = \frac{dS_{ij}}{dr_{ij}}\delta r_{ij}$$

Using the value for nearest neighbours in benzene, $dS/dr = -0{\cdot}2036$, and $\delta S = -0{\cdot}2036\delta r$.

If $\delta r = 0{\cdot}20$ Å then $\delta S = -0{\cdot}040$ and $\delta f = 0{\cdot}37$ eV. The change in one-electron energy is $2P_{ij}\delta f_{ij}$, which in this case is $\delta E_1 = 0{\cdot}506$ eV.

A similar change accompanies a small change in bond angle and can be allowed for in the same way.

B. The Change in G_{ij}

For interatomic distances less than 2·8 Å, the Coulomb integral for C—C bonds is given by the Pariser and Parr formula given in Chapter 5.

$$\gamma_{ij} = 0{\cdot}2157r_{ij}^2 - 2{\cdot}625r_{ij} + 10{\cdot}53 \quad (r \text{ in Å})$$

This leads to

$$\delta\gamma_{ij} = \frac{d\gamma_{ij}}{dr_{ij}}\delta r_{ij} = (0{\cdot}4314r_{ij} - 2{\cdot}625)\,\delta r_{ij}$$

Again considering nearest-neighbour bonds in benzene, we obtain $\delta\gamma_{ij} = -1{\cdot}071\delta r$ eV (δr in Ångström units).

The element of the total electron interaction operator G_{ij} is given by $G_{ij} = -R_{ij}\gamma_{ij}$, therefore

$$\delta G_{ij} = -R_{ij}\gamma_{ij}$$

and the change in two-electron energy is $-\frac{1}{2}P_{ij}^2\gamma_{ij}$. In our case of benzene $\delta G_{ij} = 0{\cdot}0357\delta r_{ij}$ and with $\delta r_{ij} = 0{\cdot}2$ Å (say), $\delta E_2 = 0{\cdot}048$ eV. The change in two-electron energy is therefore very small compared with the change in one-electron energy and may be ignored.

It is now possible to estimate the effect of a small change δr_{ij} on the transition energy between the ground state and the excited state. Assuming a one-configuration approximation, the transition energy E_{IJ} for a singlet transition is given by

$$E_{IJ} = \epsilon_J - \epsilon_I - J_{IJ} + 2K_{IJ}$$

Considering only the one-electron term, this becomes

$$E_{IJ} = \sum_{ij} (P'_{ij} - P_{ij}) f_{ij}$$

where P' is the charge and bond order matrix for the excited configuration.

For a small change δf_{ij} in f_{ij} (and also of course in f_{ji}) the total change in the energy is given by

$$\delta E_{IJ} = (P'_{ij} - P_{ij})\,\delta f_{ij}$$

Now $(P'_{ij} - P_{ij})$ is the difference in bond order of bond i—j in the excited and ground states, and will not usually be greater than one half, which gives an upper limit of about $\frac{1}{2}\delta f_{ij}$ for the change in one-electron energy. In our example of a change of 0·2 Å in the length of a bond in benzene, the change in transition energy δE_{IJ} is 0·2 eV. Since bond length variations in aromatic molecules are usually within 0·1 Å of the bond length of a benzene bond, the maximum error which could occur by assuming a set of standard bond lengths (i.e. those in benzene) is of the order of 0·1 eV. This is well within any accuracy which could be assigned to a calculated transition energy.

In the case of aniline, it was found that the error which is incurred by assuming a bond length of 1·393 Å for the exocyclic bond length, instead of the correct 1·47 Å, is as follows (Peacock, 1960); ΔE (ground state) 0·25 eV, and for the transition energies 0·002 eV for one and zero for the others. The inclusion of the correction thus makes a small change in the ground state energy and no significant changes to the transition energies.

References

Brown, R. D. & Heffernan, M. L. (1959). *Aust. J. Chem.* **12**, 554.

Clar, E. (1941). "Aromatische Kohlenwasserstoffe", 1st Edn. Springer-Verlag, Berlin.

Dewar, M. J. S. & Longuet-Higgins, H. C. (1954). *Proc. phys. Soc.* **A67**, 795.

Eyring, H., Walter, J. & Kimball, G. E. (1944). "Quantum Chemistry." J. Wiley and Sons Inc., New York.

Fischer-Hjalmers, I. (1962). *Ark. Fys.* **21**, 123.

Klevens, H. B. & Platt, J. R. (1949). *J. chem. Phys.* **17**, 470; see also Tech. Rept. (Pt 1), Lab. of Molec. Structure and Spectra, Chicago, U.S.A.

Kolboe, S. & Pullman, A. (1958). "Colloque International sur le Calcul des Functions d'Onde moleculaire." C.N.R.S., Paris 217.

Lefebvre, R. & Moser, C. (1956). *J. chem. Soc.* 1557, 2743.

Mataga, N. & Nishimoto, K. (1957). *Z. phys. Chem.* **13**, 140.

McWeeny, R. (1956). *Proc. R. Soc.* **A235**, 496.

McWeeny, R. & Peacock, T. E. (1957). *Proc. phys. Soc.* **A70**, 41.

Moffitt, W. E. (1954). *J. chem. Phys.* **22**, 320, 1820.

Moser, C. & Brion, H. (1955). *J. Chim. phys.* **52**, 35.

Mulliken, R. S. & Rieke, C. A. (1941). *Rep. Prog. Phys.* **8**, 231.

Pariser, R. & Parr, R. G. (1953). *J. chem. Phys.* **21**, 466, 767.

Peacock, T. E. (1959). *J. chem. Soc.* 3241.

Peacock, T. E. (1960). *Molec. Phys.* **3**, 453.

Peacock, T. E. & Wilkinson, P. T. (1962). *Proc. phys. Soc.* **79**, 105.

Peacock, T. E. & Wilkinson, P. T. (1964). *Proc. phys. Soc.* **83**, 525.

Platt, J. R. (1951). *J. chem. Phys.* **19**, 101.

Pople, J. A. (1955). *Proc. phys. Soc.* **A68**, 81.

Sidman, J. W. (1957). *J. chem. Phys.* **27**, 429.

CHAPTER 8

Electronic Spectra—II

1. Introduction

In Chapter 7 the calculation of the electronic spectra of aromatic and heterocyclic molecules using self-consistent orbitals and configuration interaction was discussed. It was seen that a satisfactory interpretation of the observed spectra could be made for a wide range of molecules. In this chapter other methods of calculating electronic spectra will be considered. Firstly, the use of Hückel orbitals with configuration interaction will be discussed. Secondly, the free-electron model will be used in an attempt to understand the spectra of the polyacene series.

2. Hückel Orbitals and Configuration Interaction

In Chapter 2 the calculation of spectra using the Hückel orbitals and the Hückel Hamiltonian was discussed. It was seen that even in its most sophisticated form, allowing configuration interaction between degenerate configurations, the theory was unable to give an adequate discussion of the spectrum. In this section the use of Hückel orbitals with a Hamiltonian constructed from them like the Hartree–Fock type will be discussed.

It is not necessary to repeat the form of the matrix elements for either the Hamiltonian or the interaction elements, these will be found in Chapters 5 and 7.

The first formulation of the theory for this type of problem was given by Goeppert-Mayer & Sklar (1938). They carried out a calculation on benzene using the form of Hamiltonian which was discussed in Chapter 5,

TABLE 35. Excited states of benzene in the Goeppert-Mayer and Sklar approximation

State	Symmetry	Energy (eV)
β, β'	$^1E_{1u}$	8·0
p	$^1B_{2u}$	5·8
α	$^1B_{1u}$	5·0

Section 1. The results of this calculation, in which only single excitations were included, are given in Table 35.

The energies of the lowest two states compare very well with the experimental values of 4·9 and 6·0 eV. The highest state, the degenerate $^1E_{1u}$ state, is about 1eV higher than the observed transition (6·8 eV). The energy order is the same as that obtained using the SCF molecular orbitals and configuration interaction discussed in the last chapter.

The next important calculation of the benzene spectrum using Hückel orbitals and configuration interaction, was that of Parr, Craig & Ross (1950). This calculation was carried out using non-empirical values of the integrals over atomic orbitals. The configuration interaction calculation included all configurations obtained by excitation of one or two electrons from the ground state, together with a few others which are associated with unusually large matrix elements with the lowest states and are important in spite of their high energies. The lowest states and their energies relative to the ground state are given in Table 36.

TABLE 36. Excited states of benzene in the Parr, Craig and Ross calculation

State	Symmetry	Energy (eV)
β, β'	$^1E_{1u}$	9·0
p	$^1E_{2g}$	7·7
α	$^1B_{2u}$	4·4

They find a lower state than the $^1E_{1u}$ state, a $^1B_{1u}$ state with an energy of 9·0 eV. They do not, however, associate this state with an observed transition and hence it was not included in the table. A very interesting feature of this calculation is that the second transition is predicted as involving the degenerate $^1E_{2g}$ as its upper state. This is in contradiction to both the Goeppert-Mayer and Sklar calculation and the semi-empirical SCF molecular orbital calculation. The energies obtained are rather unsatisfactory if it is attempted to correlate them directly with experimental data. This bears out the statement at the beginning of the last chapter that at the moment completely non-empirical calculations give rather unsatisfactory results.

It is not intended here to pursue the controversy which has persisted over many years about the symmetry of the second lowest band in benzene. Let it be sufficient to say that most theoretical calculations support an assignment of B_{2u} for the symmetry of the upper state. There is conflicting experimental evidence which supports an assignment of

E_{2g} for this state and other evidence which supports the B_{2u} assignment. The one thing which can be said about the calculations which have been reported up to the present time is that they are unable to give an unequivocal answer to this problem.

The third calculation of importance on the benzene spectrum is that of Pariser (1956a). This included configuration interaction between all configurations which arise from single electron excitations from the ground state. The Hamiltonian is constructed in the same fashion as the Hamiltonian used in the self-consistent field theory discussed in Chapter 5, with the atomic Coulomb integrals evaluated according to the Pariser–Parr method given there. The results of Pariser's calculation are given in Table 37.

TABLE 37. Excited states of benzene according to Pariser

State	Symmetry	Energy (eV)
β, β'	$^1E_{1u}$	6·548
p	$^1B_{1u}$	5·960
α	$^1B_{2u}$	4·710

The energy order given here is the familiar one with B_{1u} as the second excited level. This calculation differs from the Peacock and Wilkinson calculation (discussed in the last chapter) only in the value assumed for γ_{12}. The results of the Peacock–Wilkinson calculation are given in Table 38 for comparison. Also given in Table 38 are the results of the Pople

TABLE 38. Result of SCF MO CI calculations

State	Symmetry	Energy (eV)	
		Peacock–Wilkinson	Pople
β, β'	$^1E_{1u}$	7·10	7·00
p	$^1B_{1u}$	5·55	5·31
α	$^1B_{2u}$	4·95	5·00

(1955) calculation of the excited states of benzene which is of the same type. It can be seen that the Peacock–Wilkinson and Pople calculations give almost identical results. Pople included only single excitations between the top two filled and the bottom two empty molecular orbitals. This explains the slight disagreement between the two calculations.

One important conclusion to draw from this is the superiority of the semi-empirical approach to predict the spectra of molecules of this type.

The electronic spectra of the rest of the polyacene series has been calculated by Pariser (1956a). Again Hückel orbitals have been used and considerable configuration interaction allowed. The integrals have all been evaluated in the usual Pariser–Parr method. Pariser's results for naphthalene up to pentacene are given in Table 39.

TABLE 39. Symmetries and energies of the polyacenes using Hückel MOs and configuration interaction

	Symmetry	Energy	Experimental energy
Naphthalene	$^1B_{3u}$	32,397	31,800
	$^1B_{2u}$	36,227	34,600
	$^1B_{1g}$	44,403	45,500
	$^1A_{1g}$	46,193	52,600
Anthracene	$^1B_{2u}$	29,400	26,400
	$^1B_{3u}$	30,000	—
	$^1B_{1g}$	36,500	39,550
	$^1B_{1g}$	39,700	45,300
Naphthacene	$^1B_{2u}$	25,100	21,200
	$^1B_{3u}$	28,700	—
	$^1B_{1g}$	31,500	36,800
	$^1B_{1g}$	34,400	43,500
Pentacene	$^1B_{2u}$	22,600	17,400
	$^1B_{1g}$	27,500	
	$^1B_{3u}$	28,400	
	$^1B_{1g}$	29,700	

From an examination of Table 39 it can be seen that this method gives a reliable interpretation of the electronic spectra. One interesting molecule whose electronic spectrum has been calculated by this method is azulene (Pariser, 1956b). Azulene has been discussed previously with respect to its ground state properties. It may be recalled that azulene is isoelectronic with naphthalene, but has a five-membered ring fused with a seven-membered ring. Pariser has predicted its spectrum using Hückel orbitals and interaction between all configurations obtained by a single electron excitation from the ground state. Pariser's results are given in Table 40.

From Table 40 it can be seen that the electronic spectrum is predicted very well using this method.

TABLE 40. Symmetries and energies of the excited states of azulene

Symmetry	Energy (calc.) (eV)	Energy (expt.) (eV)
$^1B_1$	1·732	1·79
$^1A_1$	3·084	3·50
$^1B_1$	4·112	4·05
$^1A_1$	4·692	4·52

In Table 41 the electronic spectrum of pyridine is given. These results are taken from McWeeny (1957) who calculated the spectrum using Hückel orbitals for pyridine and configuration interaction between those configurations which arise from single electron excitations from the top two filled to the bottom two empty molecular orbitals of the ground state. In one way this calculation is not comparable to those given above which included much more configuration interaction. Again it can be seen that there is very good agreement between theory and experiment.

TABLE 41. Electronic spectrum of pyridine using Hückel orbitals and limited CI

Energy (calc.) (eV)	Energy (expt.) (eV)
5·018	4·9
5·842	6·2
7·085	7·0
7·217	

From the calculations reported above for a wide range of molecules it may be seen that Hückel orbitals and configuration interaction, when the elements are properly evaluated, give a good interpretation of the electronic spectrum. It is now necessary to compare the values obtained by this method with those obtained using self-consistent field molecular orbitals and configuration interaction.

3. Comparison between Hückel and Self-consistent Field MOs as a Basis for CI Calculations

A long time was spent in the last section discussing the various calculations of the electronic spectrum of benzene. The spectrum of benzene will not be discussed further in this section. Because of the close similarity in integral values a direct comparison is possible between the spectra obtained using self-consistent molecular orbitals (Peacock & Wilkinson, 1964) and Hückel orbitals (Pariser, 1956) for the polyacene series. The spectra predicted by both methods, together with the experimental values are given in Table 42.

TABLE 42. Comparison of predicted spectra of polyacenes using SCF and Hückel MOs and also with experiment

	Expt. energy	SCF MOs, nine configurations		Hückel MOs, > twenty-five configurations	
		Symmetry	Energy ($\bar{\nu}$)	Symmetry	Energy ($\bar{\nu}$)
Naphthalene	31,800	B_{3u}	35,448	B_{3u}	32,397
	34,600	B_{2u}	35,449	B_{2u}	36,227
	45,500	B_{1g}	47,972	B_{1g}	44,403
	52,600	B_{3u}	50,224	A_{1g}	46,193
Anthracene	26,400	B_{2u}	28,738	B_{2u}	29,400
	—	B_{3u}	33,147	B_{3u}	30,000
	39,550	B_{1g}	38,172	B_{1g}	36,500
	45,300	B_{1g}	43,877	B_{1g}	39,700
Naphthacene	21,200	B_{2u}	24,822	B_{2u}	25,100
	—	B_{3u}	32,440	B_{3u}	28,700
	36,800	B_{1g}	33,112	B_{1g}	31,500
	43,500	B_{1g}	38,858	B_{1g}	34,400
Pentacene	17,400	B_{2u}	22,146	B_{2u}	22,600
		B_{1g}	29,154	B_{1g}	27,500
		B_{3u}	32,303	B_{3u}	28,400
		B_{1g}	35,047	B_{1g}	29,700

It can be seen that there is very good agreement between the predicted spectra using the two methods and of both with experiment. Both methods give the same symmetries for all of the sixteen states with the exception of the upper two states for naphthalene. The energies of the states are surprisingly close, each being to within $3000\bar{\nu}$ in most cases.

The only glaring discrepancy is in the highest state of pentacene where the two methods differ by $5000\bar{\nu}$.

It is reasonable to conclude from these results that either method may be used with confidence to calculate the spectrum of a molecule of this type. It is also interesting to note that the values predicted for the *p*-band in the Pariser calculation converge to a band limit somewhere between $19{,}000\bar{\nu}$ and $20{,}000\bar{\nu}$. This is in excellent agreement with the limit predicted using the SCF MOs.

McWeeny has made a similar comparison for pyridine between the energies of the excited states using SCF MOs and Hückel MOs as a basis for a configuration interaction calculation. These results are given in Table 43.

TABLE 43. Comparison of the energies of the excited states of pyridine calculated using SCF MOs and Hückel MOs and limited configuration interaction

SCF MOs (eV)	Hückel MOs (eV)	Expt. (eV)
5·010	5·018	4·9
5·828	5·842	6·2
7·146	7·085	7·0
7·157	7·217	

Again the two calculations are in excellent agreement. The only possible objection to using self-consistent orbitals is that they over-emphasize the importance of the ground state. They are orbitals which correspond to the correct self-consistent Hamiltonian for the ground state and the excited orbitals which are used are the unoccupied or virtual orbitals which occur in the ground state calculation. However, this is no argument to support the use of Hückel orbitals in a calculation of this kind. The best way to make a calculation of this type seems to be one in which SCF orbitals for the ground state are used with limited configuration interaction. In this way it appears that the very large computational problem posed by including many configurations can be avoided. The very good agreement in the polyacene series, obtained using nine configurations formed from SCF orbitals, and the calculations based on Hückel orbitals and a minimum of twenty-five configurations, seem to suggest the value of this compromise approach. Ideally, one ought to calculate the self-consistent field solution for each excited state, but such a procedure would be tedious and probably not worth the effort.

4. The Free Electron Model

The free electron model assumes that there is a region in which electrons are free over the molecule without restriction; also, that the potential energy in this region is constant and that the electrons are confined to this region by the presence of a barrier of infinite potential energy. In other words the problem is considered to be that of the particle in a box.

In a polyene molecule the electron should be free to move over the whole length of the molecule. However, the "box" constraining the electron ought to be longer than the molecule because if this were not so the wave function would disappear at the edge of the box and there would be no probability of finding the electron on the terminal atoms. This would clearly be unrealistic on physical considerations. The electron path must be longer than the extent of the molecule and it has become conventional to choose the length to be one bond length further than the terminal atom at each end.

Considering a polyene as a "particle in a box", the wave equation is

$$-\frac{h^2}{8\pi^2 m}\cdot\frac{d^2\psi}{dx} = E\psi \quad (0 \leqslant x \leqslant a) \tag{1}$$

where a is the length of the box and x is a point inside the box. The solution of this equation is well known and is

$$\psi_n = \sqrt{2/a}\sin\frac{\pi n}{a}x \quad (0 \leqslant x \leqslant a) \tag{2}$$

n is a quantum number and can take the values 0, 1, 2, 3.... To each value of n there is a corresponding energy which is:

$$E_n = \frac{n^2 h^2}{8ma^2} \tag{3}$$

In a conjugated molecule containing k double bonds there are $2k$ π-electrons. These are just sufficient to fill k levels in the ground state. The first excited state arises when one of these electrons is promoted from the kth to the $(k+1)$th level. The transition energy is

$$\Delta E = E_{k+1} - E_k = \frac{(k+1)^2 h^2}{8ma^2} - \frac{k^2 h^2}{8ma^2}$$

$$= \frac{(2k+1)h^2}{8ma^2} \tag{4}$$

After inserting values of the constants this becomes

$$\Delta E = \frac{(2k+1)}{33a^2} \times 10^7 \bar{\nu} \tag{5}$$

where a is expressed in Ångströms. Assuming an average bond length of 1·4 Å, (5) becomes

$$\Delta E = \frac{2k+1}{64{\cdot}68(2k+1)^2}10^7 = \frac{10^7}{64{\cdot}68(2k+1)}\bar{\nu} \qquad (6)$$

The energy of the first excited state for the first four polyenes is given in Table 44.

TABLE 44. Lowest electronic transition for the polyenes

	Predicted energy ($\bar{\nu}$)	Observed energy ($\bar{\nu}$)
Ethylene	51,500	61,500
Butadiene	31,000	46,080
Hexatriene	22,100	39,750
Octatetraene	17,250	35,000

It is clear that the free electron method does not give good predictions of polyene spectra. As a qualitative guide it is fairly satisfactory. However, even here it is unsatisfactory because as k tends to infinity the energy of the lowest transition will tend to zero. This is in contradiction to the observed facts. As was discussed earlier, the spectra of the polyenes converge to a lower limit.

The lack of agreement with experiment may be due to the uncertainty in the determination of a, and to the assumption of a uniform potential along the whole path, which is certainly wrong.

Onc advantage of the method, however, is that it allows a pictorial interpretation of the various "orbitals" in terms of waves and nodes. To this extent the method is useful.

Platt (1949) has extended the theory to the polyacene type of molecule. Platt assumes that to a first approximation the molecules may be considered to be circular. The electron is then free to move along the circumference of the circle. The approximation of the path length is now removed. The path length is the circumference of the circle. The only boundary condition required now is that the wave function is continuous around the path. The wave functions for this type of problem are also well known and have the form

$$\psi = e^{im_q\phi} \qquad (7)$$

where $m_q = 0, \pm 1, \pm 2$, etc., and ϕ is the polar angle about the centre of the circle. The energies of these wave functions are given by

$$E = \frac{q^2 h^2}{2ml^2} = 1{\cdot}2 \times 10^6 q^2/l^2 \text{ cm}^{-1} \qquad (8)$$

where l is the length around the perimeter in Ångströms and q is a quantum number having integral positive values 0, 1, 2...n, and is a measure of angular momentum about the central axis possessed by the electron. From (8) it can be seen that the energy varies with the square of q. All levels except the first (where $q=0$) are doubly degenerate, depending upon whether the electron is considered to rotate in a positive or negative sense. In a molecule containing $4n+2$ electrons the z component of the angular momentum for all of the electrons m_q will be zero. This is the case for all of the polyacenes where the number of π-electrons is $4n+2$ if n is the number of rings.

The selection rule for transitions is $\Delta m_q = 1$. Thus transitions of the type $m_q \rightarrow m_q + 1$ and $-m_q \rightarrow -(m_q+1)$ are allowed, whilst transitions of the type $m_q \rightarrow -(m_q+1)$ and $-m_q \rightarrow m_q+1$ which involve $\Delta m_q = 2m_q+1$ are forbidden. This selection rule leads to every transition being doubly degenerate. There is an analogy here with the molecular orbital method where transitions of the type $A \rightarrow B'$ are degenerate. It is possible, however, to split each of these degenerate excited states.

Moffitt (1954) reformulated the perimeter model theory, as this theory was called, and put it on a more quantitative foundation. In Moffitt's version the approximation becomes formally similar to the antisymmetrized molecular orbital treatment. Moffitt made a comparative study of the polyacene series and found that the p-band converged to a limit of about 18,000$\bar{\nu}$, the α-band to a limit of about 20,000$\bar{\nu}$ and the β-band to about 32,000$\bar{\nu}$. It may be seen that these values are almost identical to those found in the SCF MO CI method for the p-band.

Pariser (1956) has carried out perimeter MO calculations on naphthalene. He used the same integral values as were used in the Hückel orbital calculations. The two calculations are directly comparable. The two sets of values for the lowest states are given in Table 45.

TABLE 45. Electronic excited states for naphthalene calculated using SCF MOs, Hückel MOs and perimeter MOs together with the experimental values

SCF MO ($\bar{\nu}$)		Hückel MO ($\bar{\nu}$)		Perimeter MO ($\bar{\nu}$)		Expt. ($\bar{\nu}$)
B_{3u}	35,448	B_{3u}	32,397	B_{3u}	36,600	31,800
B_{2u}	35,449	B_{2u}	36,227	B_{2u}	41,000	34,600
B_{1g}	47,972	B_{1g}	44,403	B_{1g}	48,900	45,500
B_{3u}	50,224	A_{1g}	46,193	B_{1g}	51,200	52,600

Table 45 indicates that the perimeter MO method when properly applied is not too bad. For the two lower states it is some 5000$\bar{\nu}$ too high while for the next two states the predicted values are in good agreement with experiment. Although this is pleasing, one must bear in mind that the simple picture has been lost and ask if there is any point in using a model such as this whose main appeal was to produce a pictorial representation of what was taking place.

Pariser (1956b) has also calculated the spectrum of azulene using the perimeter MO method. His results are given in Table 46 together with his results using the Hückel model.

TABLE 46. Excited electronic states for azulene using Hückel MOs and perimeter MOs together with the experimental values

Hückel model (eV)		Perimeter model (eV)		Expt. (eV)
B_1	1·732	B_1	2·814	1·79
A_1	3·084	A_1	4·194	3·50
B_1	4·112	B_1	5·095	4·05
A_1	4·692	A_1	6·250	4·52

From an examination of the energies in Table 46 it can be seen that the perimeter MO method gives no real quantitative interpretation of the azulene spectrum. While it gives the same sequence of states symmetry-wise as the Hückel model, the values of the energy bear no real relation to reality.

5. Concluding Remarks

In this chapter the methods of calculating spectra using methods other than those involving self-consistent field molecular orbitals have been discussed. It has been shown that, provided that enough configurations are used, Hückel orbitals can give results which are as good as those obtained using self-consistent orbitals and more limited configuration interaction.

We also looked at the free electron model and saw that, while it gave a pictorial representation of what happened during a transition, the values obtained for the transition energy are at best only semi-quantitative.

Several methods of calculating spectra have not been discussed. It is possible to understand the spectrum of a derivative by taking the diagonal elements of the configuration interaction matrix to be the observed transition energies and introducing the effects of the substituent by perturbation theory. The theory of charge-transfer spectra has not been discussed. This is partly because this is a very limited field and partly because, like the other case given above, it has no real place in a work such as this.

It has been shown that a quantitative understanding of the spectra of the polyacene and polyazine spectra can be obtained using the semi-empirical methods discussed in the last two chapters. Since these two series are typical of aromatic molecules, it is reasonable to assert that confidence may be placed in calculations of the electronic spectra of aromatic molecules along these lines.

References

Goeppert-Mayer, M. & Sklar, A. L. (1938). *J. chem. Phys.* **6**, 645.
McWeeny, R. (1957). *Proc. phys. Soc.* **A70**, 593.
Moffitt, W. E. (1954). *J. chem. Phys.* **22**, 320, 1820.
Pariser, R. (1956a). *J. chem. Phys.* **24**, 250.
Pariser, R. (1956b). *J. chem. Phys.* **25**, 1112.
Parr, R. G., Craig, D. P. & Ross, I. G. (1950). *J. chem. Phys.* **18**, 1561.
Peacock, T. E. & Wilkinson, P. T. (1964). *Proc. phys. Soc.* **83**, 525.
Platt, J. R. (1949). *J. chem. Phys.* **17**, 484.
Pople, J. A. (1955). *Proc. phys. Soc.* **A68**, 81.

Appendix

The Use of Symmetry Orbitals to Reduce the Size of the Secular Determinant; the Use of Group Theory to Obtain Symmetry Orbitals

In Chapter 2 the use of symmetry orbitals was discussed. It was seen that these led to considerable reduction in the size of the secular determinant. In certain cases, e.g. benzene and cyclobutadiene, complete factorization occurs which makes the solution trivial and the orbitals are completely determined by symmetry.

In this appendix, symmetry orbitals will be systematically determined using group theory.

Consider the butadiene molecule

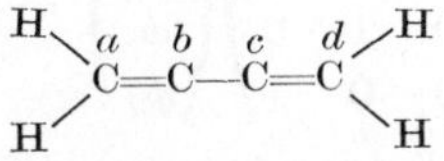

The first step is to find the representation of the appropriate point group for which the set of $2p_z$-orbitals ϕ_a, ϕ_b, ϕ_c and ϕ_d forms a basis. The point group of the molecule is C_{2v} which has the operations E—the identity, C_2—the rotation through 180° about the twofold axis, σ_h—reflection in the plane of the molecule and σ_v—reflection in the plane perpendicular to the plane of the molecule which includes the twofold rotation axis.

First we write down the regular representation for the set of orbitals. This is done in the following way (see, e.g., H. Jones, 1960, "The Theory of Brillouin Zones and Electronic States in Crystals", p. 76, North-Holland Publishing Company, Amsterdam). The operation σ_v interchanges orbitals ϕ_a and ϕ_d, ϕ_b and ϕ_c. This can be written down in the following way

$$\begin{pmatrix} 0 & 0 & 0 & 1 \\ 0 & 0 & 1 & 0 \\ 0 & 1 & 0 & 0 \\ 1 & 0 & 0 & 0 \end{pmatrix} \begin{pmatrix} \phi_a \\ \phi_b \\ \phi_c \\ \phi_d \end{pmatrix} = \begin{pmatrix} \phi_d \\ \phi_c \\ \phi_b \\ \phi_a \end{pmatrix}$$

The operation σ_h is the reflection of the set of orbitals in the plane of the molecule and therefore causes each orbital to change (because the

p-orbitals are antisymmetric across the plane of the molecule). This operation can be represented by

$$\begin{pmatrix} -1 & 0 & 0 & 0 \\ 0 & -1 & 0 & 0 \\ 0 & 0 & -1 & 0 \\ 0 & 0 & 0 & -1 \end{pmatrix} \begin{pmatrix} \phi_a \\ \phi_b \\ \phi_c \\ \phi_d \end{pmatrix} = \begin{pmatrix} -\phi_a \\ -\phi_b \\ -\phi_c \\ -\phi_d \end{pmatrix}$$

The operation C_2 interchanges ϕ_a and ϕ_d also ϕ_b and ϕ_c, but in addition also causes a change in sign because of the antisymmetry of the p-orbitals across the plane of the molecule. The matrix equation which represents this operation is

$$\begin{pmatrix} 0 & 0 & 0 & -1 \\ 0 & 0 & -1 & 0 \\ 0 & -1 & 0 & 0 \\ -1 & 0 & 0 & 0 \end{pmatrix} \begin{pmatrix} \phi_a \\ \phi_b \\ \phi_c \\ \phi_d \end{pmatrix} = \begin{pmatrix} -\phi_d \\ -\phi_c \\ -\phi_b \\ -\phi_a \end{pmatrix}$$

Finally, for the identity operation which leaves everything unchanged, we have

$$\begin{pmatrix} 1 & 0 & 0 & 0 \\ 0 & 1 & 0 & 0 \\ 0 & 0 & 1 & 0 \\ 0 & 0 & 0 & 1 \end{pmatrix} \begin{pmatrix} \phi_a \\ \phi_b \\ \phi_c \\ \phi_d \end{pmatrix} = \begin{pmatrix} \phi_a \\ \phi_b \\ \phi_c \\ \phi_d \end{pmatrix}$$

This set of four matrices form a representation of the group C_{2v} which is called the regular representation, and is the representation appropriate to the basis of four $2p_z$-orbitals.

The regular representation can be written

$$\underset{E}{\begin{pmatrix} 1 & 0 & 0 & 0 \\ 0 & 1 & 0 & 0 \\ 0 & 0 & 1 & 0 \\ 0 & 0 & 0 & 1 \end{pmatrix}} \underset{C_2}{\begin{pmatrix} 0 & 0 & 0 & -1 \\ 0 & 0 & -1 & 0 \\ 0 & -1 & 0 & 0 \\ -1 & 0 & 0 & 0 \end{pmatrix}} \underset{\sigma_v}{\begin{pmatrix} 0 & 0 & 0 & 1 \\ 0 & 0 & 1 & 0 \\ 0 & 1 & 0 & 0 \\ 1 & 0 & 0 & 0 \end{pmatrix}} \underset{\sigma_h}{\begin{pmatrix} -1 & 0 & 0 & 0 \\ 0 & -1 & 0 & 0 \\ 0 & 0 & -1 & 0 \\ 0 & 0 & 0 & -1 \end{pmatrix}}$$

The character for this representation, which is the sum of the diagonal elements of each matrix, is

E	C_2	σ_v	σ_h
4	0	0	-4

The characters of the irreducible representation of C_{2v} are

	E	C_2	σ_v	σ_h
A_1	1	1	1	1
A_2	1	1	-1	-1
B_1	1	-1	1	-1
B_2	1	-1	-1	1

The number of times each irreducible representation occurs in the reducible representation is given by

$$a_i = h^{-1} \Sigma \chi_i(R)\chi(R)$$

where the summation is carried out over all of the operations of the group. h is the order, i.e. the number of operations, in the group. In our case we find

$$a_{A_1} = \tfrac{1}{4}\{4.1+0.1+0.1-4.1\} = 0$$
$$a_{A_2} = \tfrac{1}{4}\{4.1+0.1+0.(-1)-4.(-1)\} = 2$$
$$a_{B_1} = \tfrac{1}{4}\{4.1+0.(-1)+0.1-4.(-1)\} = 2$$
$$a_{B_2} = \tfrac{1}{4}\{4.1+0.(-1)+0.(-1)-4.1\} = 0$$

The representations A_2 and B_1 thus occur twice each and the other two are absent in this representation. There are therefore two molecular orbitals of symmetry A_2 and two of B_1.

The next step is to construct the combinations of the atomic orbitals which transform like the respective representations.

Consider first the A_2 type. Under the operation E orbitals remain unchanged. Under the operation C_2 orbitals ϕ_a and ϕ_d change place and sign, under the operation σ_v orbitals ϕ_a and ϕ_d change place but not sign, and finally under operation σ_h the orbitals both stay in their places but the functions change sign.

Let us see what happens to the function $(1/\sqrt{2})(\phi_a-\phi_d)$ under each of the operations. Under E the function is unchanged, under C_{2v} it becomes $(1/\sqrt{2})(-\phi_d+\phi_a)$ and hence remains unchanged, under σ_v it becomes $(1/\sqrt{2})(\phi_d-\phi_a)$ and thus changes sign, and finally under σ_h it becomes $(1/\sqrt{2})(-\phi_a+\phi_d)$ and the function changes sign. The same sequence applies to the function $(1/\sqrt{2})(\phi_b-\phi_c)$.

The two functions $(1/\sqrt{2})(\phi_a-\phi_d)$ and $(1/\sqrt{2})(\phi_b-\phi_c)$ thus transform like the representation A_2. It is found that the functions $(1/\sqrt{2})(\phi_a+\phi_d)$ and $(1/\sqrt{2})(\phi_b+\phi_c)$ transform like B_1. The four symmetry orbitals which are appropriate to this molecule are therefore

$$\left.\begin{matrix}\frac{1}{\sqrt{2}}(\phi_a-\phi_d)\\[2ex] \frac{1}{\sqrt{2}}(\phi_b-\phi_c)\end{matrix}\right\}A_2 \qquad \left.\begin{matrix}\frac{1}{\sqrt{2}}(\phi_b+\phi_c)\\[2ex] \frac{1}{\sqrt{2}}(\phi_a+\phi_d)\end{matrix}\right\}B_1$$

These symmetry orbitals are the same as those found in Chapter 2, Section 6. The solution of the problem then follows the same course as discussed there. It is useful to remember that the element of the

Hamiltonian between symmetry orbitals which belong to different irreducible representations of the point group is zero. This therefore saves considerable labour in working out the matrix elements.

The enumeration of the symmetry orbitals for any molecule follows these lines. The use of the regular representation and the systematic construction of the symmetry orbitals is a much surer approach than the intuitive method discussed in Chapter 2, Section 6. For certain molecules it is impossible to write down the symmetry orbitals by inspection. This is the case whenever two-dimensional representations are involved. Under these circumstances the symmetry orbitals must be systematically constructed. We shall now do this for *sym*-triazine.

sym-Triazine has a three-fold rotation axis perpendicular to the plane of the ring. Rotation about this axis interchanges the carbon or the nitrogen $2p_z$-orbitals among themselves. In addition to the C_{3v}-axis there are three in-plane twofold rotation axes. These axes pass through a carbon and a nitrogen atom which lie across the ring from each other, e.g. through a and d or b and e or c and f. In the first case this interchanges f and b and also c and e. There are then three other operations which involve reflections. σ_h is the operation which reflects across the plane of the molecule. There are three planes σ_v which are perpendicular to the plane of the molecule, these include the twofold axes. One plane includes the a–d axis, the second plane includes the b–e axis and the third the c–f axis. Finally there is the operation S_3, which is a rotation through 120° about the threefold axis followed by reflection across the plane of the molecule, i.e. C_3 followed by σ_h. There are two of these operations depending upon whether the rotation is clockwise or anticlockwise.

The character table for this point group, D_{3h}, is given below.

	E	$2C_3$	$3C_2$	σ_h	$2S_3$	$3\sigma_v$
A_1'	1	1	1	1	1	1
A_2'	1	1	-1	1	1	-1
E'	2	-1	0	2	-1	0
A_1''	1	1	1	-1	-1	-1
A_2''	1	1	-1	-1	-1	1
E''	2	-1	0	-2	1	0

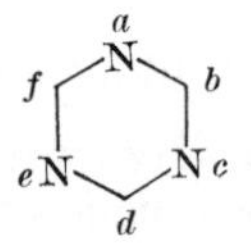

Proceeding as before, the regular representation for which the six $2p_z$-orbitals form a basis can be written down. The characters of this representation are found to be

$$6 \quad 0 \quad -6 \quad -6 \quad 0 \quad 6$$

This representation contains the following irreducible representations

$$\Gamma_{\text{mol}} = 2A_2'' + 2E''$$

The symmetry orbitals which transform like A_2'' can be found as before, and are

$$\frac{1}{\sqrt{3}}(a+c+e) \quad \text{and} \quad \frac{1}{\sqrt{3}}(b+d+f)$$

To find the orbitals which transform like the two-dimensional representation is a little more complicated. Consider first the set of three nitrogen orbitals. One combination which has the correct symmetry properties is

$$\frac{1}{\sqrt{6}}(2a-c-e)$$

Another symmetry orbital is required from the same set of orbitals and this can be written

$$\frac{1}{\sqrt{6}}(-a+2c-e)$$

Unfortunately these two symmetry orbitals are not orthogonal. It is therefore necessary to find a pair which are. This is done as follows. First evaluate the overlap integral S, this is found to be $-\frac{1}{2}$. Assume that $(1/\sqrt{6})(2a-c-e)$ is one of the correct orbitals (this choice is arbitrary), the orbital orthogonal to it is then

$$\frac{1}{\sqrt{6}}\{(-a+2c-e)-(-\tfrac{1}{2})(2a-c-e)\}$$

which, on normalization, gives $(1/\sqrt{2})(c-e)$ as the other symmetry orbital.

Considering the three carbon $2p_z$-orbitals, it is found that the symmetry orbitals are

$$\frac{1}{\sqrt{6}}(-b+2d-f)$$

and

$$\frac{1}{\sqrt{2}}(b-f)$$

The symmetry orbitals can therefore be written

$$\begin{array}{lll}
A_2'' & \dfrac{1}{\sqrt{3}}(a+c+e) & \dfrac{1}{\sqrt{3}}(b+d+f) \\[2ex]
E'' & \left.\begin{array}{l}\dfrac{1}{\sqrt{6}}(2a-c-e) \\[2ex] \dfrac{1}{\sqrt{6}}(-b+2d-f)\end{array}\right\} & \left\{\begin{array}{l}\dfrac{1}{\sqrt{2}}(c-e) \\[2ex] \dfrac{1}{\sqrt{2}}(b-f)\end{array}\right.
\end{array}$$

The solution of the problem then follows the usual lines.

It can be seen from these two examples that the use of symmetry orbitals leads to a considerable simplification of the secular determinant. It is found that in the case of butadiene the four-by-four problem becomes two two-by-two problems. In the case of *sym*-triazine, however, the simplification is astonishing. At first sight the six-by-six determinant factorizes to give one two-by-two and one four-by-four. However, on evaluating the matrix elements it is found that the four-by-four factorizes into two two-by-two determinants, $(1/\sqrt{6})(2a-c-e)$ and $(1/\sqrt{6})(-b+2d-f)$ interact to give one determinant and $(1/\sqrt{2})(c-e)$ and $(1/\sqrt{2})(b-f)$ interact to give the other, all other elements are zero. The symmetry orbitals for *sym*-triazine could not have been written down by inspection, the only way to generate them is by the use of the systematic group theoretical method discussed above.

Author Index

Numbers in italics are the pages on which the references are listed.

Subject Index

C

D

E

I

K

L

M